SCPMG...the first fifty years

SCPMG...the first fifty years

history of the
SOUTHERN CALIFORNIA PERMANENTE MEDICAL GROUP

1953–2003

Teri Ann Allen

This book was a collaborative project with the Southern California Permanente Medical Group and Kaiser Permanente MultiMedia Communications, Southern California.

Project Sponsors: Les Zendle, MD and Terry Bream, RN, MN
Art Direction and Design: Grace Hauser
Design and Production: Bob Turko
Research: Gerald Barnes
Production Coordination: Stephen Beebe
Editor: Janet Howard

PAGE 3
TOP LEFT
Jim Vohs with Ray Kay, MD
BOTTOM
Henry J. Kaiser, standing at left, with his executives

For information contact:
Kaiser Permanente
MultiMedia Communications
825 Colorado Blvd. #319
Los Angeles CA 90041
phone: 323-259-4546

Library of Congress Catalogue Card Number: 2003112688
ISBN NO: 0-9744474-0-4

CONTENTS

ACKNOWLEDGMENTS

THANK YOU to the following individuals for their support in creating this book. Each person was always available to answer questions, review copy, or provide photographs and, above all, share their experiences, memories and expertise.

Terry Bream, RN, MN
Adrienne Cotterell
Tom Debley
Paul Deiter, MD
Vincent Felitti, MD
Hal Frankl, MD
Ann Geiger, PhD
Oliver Goldsmith, MD
Irwin Goldstein, MD
Kurt Hauser
Irv Klitsner, MD
Jean Lawrence, Sc.D
Jo Ann Lesser
Adrienne Leyva
George Longstreth, MD
Gary Lulejian, MD
Raymond Marcus, MD
Frank Murray, MD
Michael A. Neri, MD
Larry Oates, MD
Peter Pellerito
Diana Petitti, MD
Richard Rajaratnam, MD
James Roorda, MD
Joseph Ruderman, MD
Ann Ryder
Noreen Schob
Mei Ling Schwartz
Rick Tilley
Jeffrey Weisz, MD
Judy White
Robert Zeiger, MD, PhD

Three people must be singled out for a special thank you, Les Zendle, MD, Sam Sapin, MD, and Steve Gilford.

Dr. Les Zendle, SCPMG's Associate Medical Director of Clinical Services from 1993 through 2003, guided the creation of this book from its inception through completion. He continually reviewed content and made many valuable additions to the text. He quickly responded to any requests for interviews, information and assistance. He facilitated interviews with many of the people consulted in the writing of this book. His dedication and support throughout are greatly appreciated.

Dr. Sam Sapin, who served in many important positions with SCPMG from 1955 until his retirement in 1989, brought a unique perspective and depth of knowledge to his review of this manuscript. Dr. Sapin was always happy to talk, review ideas or answer any question, and if he didn't have the answer (a rare occurrence!) he knew where to find it.

His remarkable memory, generous spirit and personal storehouse of documents were indispensable in the preparation of this book.

Steve Gilford, Kaiser Permanente historian, carefully reviewed the manuscript and made many valuable suggestions to enrich its content. Steve has sought out many Kaiser Permanente pioneers with whom he has conducted lengthy and insightful interviews. Many of these individuals had never been interviewed before, so it's to Steve's credit that we now have a record of thoughts and experiences that would otherwise have been lost. Steve generously shared many of these interviews with the writer and they add immeasurably to the narrative.

PREFACE

D R. Sidney Garfield once described the relationship between Dr. Ray Kay and the Southern California Permanente Medical Group (SCPMG) with the adage, "Every great institution is the lengthened shadow of one great man." Indeed, Drs. Kay and Garfield, as well as numerous other Permanente Medicine "pioneers" whom you will come to know through this book, continue to cast their shadows over SCPMG. It is their vision, spirit and dedication throughout the last 50 years that have made our Medical Group the unique organization it is today. SCPMG has been a trailblazer in American medicine and continues to demonstrate the benefits of a physician self-governed group practice to the health care world.

I have great respect and awe for this organization and its people, both past and present. We have a proud history rooted in the values of idealism, pragmatism and innovation, but most importantly, we have a deep concern for our patients and the communities we serve. The wisdom and fortitude conveyed in this historical volume is our legacy, and it is this legacy that will guide us through the next 50 years.

— *Oliver Goldsmith, MD*
SCPMG Medical Director

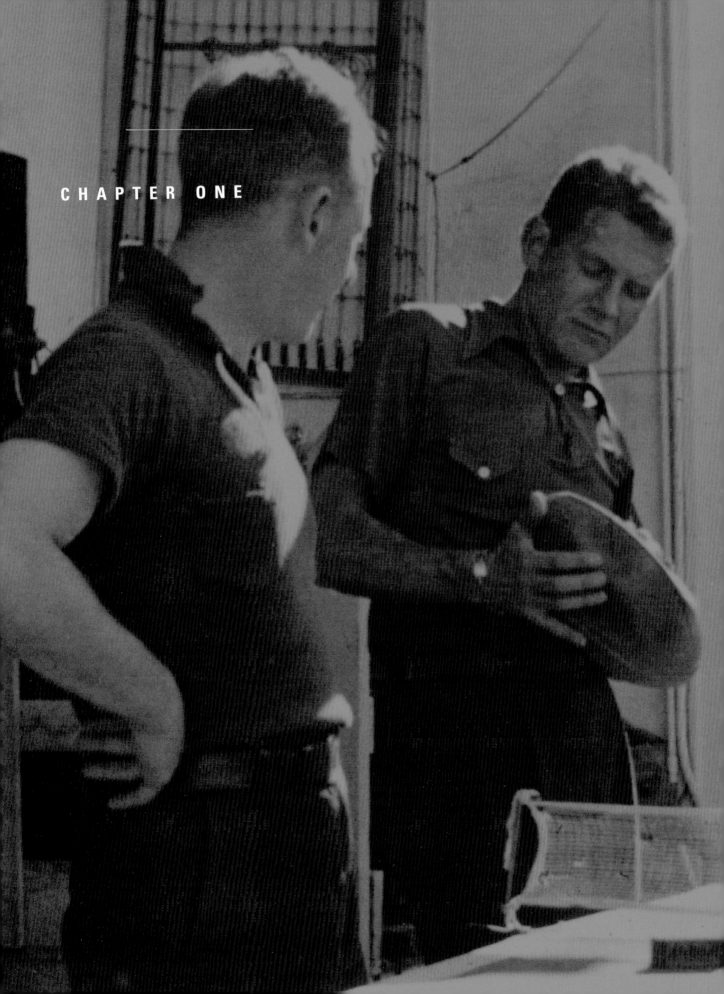

CHAPTER ONE

THE DREAMERS

SIDNEY GARFIELD AND RAYMOND KAY
They had dreamed together about removing the economic barriers to medical care. They dreamed of developing a system of medical care that would make it possible for doctors to rid themselves of increasing administrative details and devote their full energies to the care of patients. They dreamed of a system where continuing education would be a top priority and doctors could consult freely in order to enhance the quality of care. They believed that pre-paid group practice offered a way to accomplish all of these goals.[1]

ALTHOUGH the Southern California Permanente Medical Group became an official partnership on January 1, 1953, it did not spring to life in a single day. The guiding principles of the organization took decades to develop; decades of stops and starts, of successes and failures. Above all, it took the persistence, extraordinary vision and dreams of two men, Sidney Garfield and Raymond Kay.

Sidney Garfield and Ray Kay were both just beginning their medical careers when they met in the early 1930s at Los Angeles County General Hospital (now the Los Angeles County/USC Medical Center). The origins of SCPMG may well have been right then and there. As Ray Kay would later say, "Many fundamental concepts of the Southern California Permanente Medical Group stem from the early experience and reactions some of us had while young physicians in training at the Los Angeles County General Hospital."[2]

Sidney Garfield would go on to pioneer the health care delivery system we now know as Kaiser Permanente, while Ray Kay would become the driving force behind the formation of SCPMG and its first Medical Director.

Ironically, neither Sidney Garfield nor Raymond Kay grew up dreaming of a career in medicine.

LEFT
Ray Kay, MD and Sidney Garfield, MD during one of Dr. Kay's visits to Contractors General Hospital

SIDNEY ROY GARFIELD, MD

SIDNEY ROY GARFIELD was born in Elizabeth, New Jersey on April 17, 1906 to Isaac and Bertha Garfield, who had emigrated from Russia as a young couple. By the time Sidney was born, his parents had worked their way up from poverty to become successful clothing store owners. By all accounts, the red-headed Sidney was a lively and precocious youngster. When he was 4 years old, his parents passed him off as a much older and wiser 5-year-old to get him into the local public school. Sidney was a whiz at science and math and dreamed of becoming an engineer or architect.

But by the time Sidney was ready for college, his parents had other plans for him. They had heard that the State of New Jersey was giving exams for scholarships to Rutgers University. If Sidney could pass the exam, he could get a full scholarship to study medicine, so medicine it would be.

Sidney's sister Sally describes a memorable confrontation between her brother and their parents when they insisted he give up his engineering and architectural ambitions to become a doctor. According to Sally, Sidney initially found the prospect of a medical career terrifying. She remembers him sobbing as he tearfully explained that he couldn't stand the sight of blood. He begged his parents to let him study something else, but their wishes prevailed.[3]

Sidney passed the exam and was awarded his full scholarship to Rutgers. In 1923, when his family moved to Los Angeles, he transferred to the University of Southern California. He graduated with a B.S. degree from USC in 1924, then applied to five of the best medical schools in the country. Four turned him down; the fifth, the University of Iowa, accepted him.[4] He received his MD degree from Iowa in 1928 and headed off for a one-year internship at the Michael Reese Hospital in Chicago. Sidney returned to LA in 1929 where he'd been offered a three-year residency in surgery at the Los Angeles County General Hospital. Years later, Sally Garfield said that her brother never regretted going to medical school.[5]

LEFT
1928: 22-year-old Sidney Garfield graduating from University of Iowa Medical School

ABOVE
Sidney with movie star Alice Faye at Arrowhead Springs Resort. She called the young surgeon her "favorite cutter-upper"

RAYMOND KAY, MD

TOP RIGHT
Raymond Kosminsky of Marshall, Texas, dressed as a frontiersman

ABOVE
Raymond Kay as a child with his mother and father

BELOW
Letter of recommendation to Stanford from one of Ray Kay's high school teachers

FAR RIGHT TOP
Military Cadet, age 12

FAR RIGHT BELOW
Stanford student photograph, circa 1924, age 20

RAYMOND MYER KOSMINSKY was born on August 28, 1904 in Texarkana, Texas. His father, Louis, sold cotton, while his mother, Hallette, was a housewife. His father died when Ray was just four years old, so he and his mother moved in with her parents who owned a successful department store in Marshall, Texas. The living arrangement was a happy one and would continue for many years, as Ray's mother never remarried. For several years, the family vacationed in Southern California before finally buying a house in Ocean Park, near Venice, in 1912. They promptly enrolled Ray in the Santa Monica Military School. "I was a pretty spoiled brat," Ray would later say, "they thought I needed a man's hand."[6]

At first, Ray hated military school but eventually came to enjoy it, especially because of the friendships he developed with the other students. In 1917, a deadly flu epidemic hit Los Angeles, closing the schools and causing Ray and his family to move back to Marshall where Ray started high school. After a year in Marshall, the family returned to California where Ray finished his secondary education at Los Angeles High School.

When interviewed by Ora Huth in 1985 for the Kaiser Permanente Oral History Project, Ray Kay remembered his childhood with affection and credited his grandparents with helping transform the self-described "spoiled brat" into a responsible adult. "My grandparents played a very important part in my life," Kay recalled, "especially my grandmother, who was a homeopath, who believed in and was very, very interested in medicine. [. . .] she'd used acanthine (aconite and belladonna) and all that. You know, a homeopath uses very small doses of everything, so she never hurt anybody with it." When asked about the effectiveness of his grandmother's homeopathic remedies, Kay answered as a physician with 50-plus years of experience, "They're like most medicine, you know. It's the way you give it rather than what you give that counts."[7]

In spite of Kay's closeness to his grandmother and her interest in medicine, he did not anticipate a medical career. In fact, he was being groomed to take over the family department store in Marshall. But when he learned that a doctor might have been partially to blame for the death of a friend's mother, he changed his plans. "So at that time," said Kay, "I made up my mind. I thought, 'Well, by gosh, I'm not happy about the idea of just making money running the store all my life.' I didn't think that would hold my interest. So I started thinking that I would like to go into medicine, but I really had not had scientific courses or anything similar. I didn't know if I would be any good in science. But I decided that, 'By George, at least I would be conscientious, and I wouldn't hurt anybody by neglecting them like that.'"[8]

Ray Kay earned his medical degree from Stanford University in 1932, then started an internship at Los Angeles County General Hospital.

MEETING OF THE MINDS

Ray Kay and Sidney Garfield became friends while at LA County, along with Kay's roommate Justin Wallace Neighbor. In 1942, Dr. Wally Neighbor would become chief executive officer and medical director of the Northwest Permanente Foundation. Later, he would become a charter partner of The Permanente Medical Group in Northern California and serve as a permanent member of the Executive Committee until his retirement.

While LA County worked to prepare most of its young physicians for solo practice, it did so within a group environment that Garfield and Kay soon grew to appreciate. "When he [Garfield] was on duty at night as a surgical resident seeing all the acute abdomens and other acute cases," remembered Kay, "I would very frequently join him, and I learned a tremendous amount. Likewise, he would spend a lot of time with me in my medical wards and we would learn from each other. And we felt that one of the wonderful things about our training was that we learned from each other, that we shared our patients, and shared our knowledge, and learned a great deal. And we thought, 'Wouldn't it be wonderful if we could practice medicine that way, and have that fellowship and that learning develop from each other?'"[9]

Garfield and Kay were also impressed by the ability to practice without economic blocks. "Whatever the patient needed we could do for them," said Kay. "Whatever we needed — the labwork, the X-rays, or to diagnose them, or to treat them — we were able to do, and there was nothing that stopped us. That seemed to be wonderful. We then started thinking, 'Wouldn't it be wonderful if we could really practice as a doctor with a group of doctors where you could share knowledge, and share experience, and share patients, and where you could take care of people with no economic blocks?' So I reckon way back there we were dreaming of it a little bit."[10]

Although they were beginning to dream of group practice, both Ray Kay and Sidney Garfield set out to establish their own traditional fee-for-service practices after leaving LA County. But in the midst of the Great Depression, Kay soon found himself treating many patients who were unable to pay. He knew that some physicians made up for the shortfall by providing patients who could pay with more care than necessary and charging them accordingly. That was not Ray Kay's style.

He also missed the challenge and stimulation of working with other physicians. For Ray Kay, the solution was to limit his fee-for-service practice to half-time and return to LA County Hospital as a staff physician and teacher of interns and residents.

1904

Raymond Kay born on August 28 in Texarkana, Texas.

1906

Sidney Garfield born on April 17 in Elizabeth, New Jersey

SIDNEY GARFIELD AND THE ORIGINS OF PREPAYMENT

Sidney Garfield had also tried to establish a private practice in Los Angeles but found the Great Depression against him as well. Dr. Garfield needed a job. He heard about one in Indio, California where the Metropolitan Water District of Los Angeles was building a great aqueduct to bring Colorado River water to LA. The MWD needed a physician to run their small clinic in Indio, a little town at the edge of the Mojave Desert.

He thought he might be their man and went to Indio to check into it, but when the MWD offered him $125 a month, he turned them down, believing that his skills were worth at least $300 a month. Before heading back to Los Angeles, Garfield decided to stay in Indio long enough to visit Dr. Gene Morris. Morris had trained under Garfield at LA County Hospital and was now practicing as an assistant to an older physician who was running a small hospital in an old Victorian home. Morris was unhappy with the arrangement and had been looking around for a new business opportunity. "What about setting up out in the desert to take care of the construction workers?" he asked Garfield. Sidney Garfield went out to the construction site in the Mojave Desert to look around — Morris was right, if any place needed medical care, this was it.

The project was massive, the work brutal and dangerous. There were thousands of men living and working in the desert to build the dams, tunnels and canals along the 242-mile aqueduct route. And while the construction workers did have compensation insurance

Los Angeles County Hospital

1932

Sidney Garfield and Raymond Kay meet at Los Angeles County General Hospital and envision the kind of group practice that would become the Southern California Permanente Medical Group

1934

Sidney Garfield introduces a prepaid medical care program to workers on the Colorado River Aqueduct project in the Mojave Desert

1938

Impressed by Sidney Garfield's prepayment program in southern California, Henry J. Kaiser asks him to set up a similar program for workers on Kaiser's Grand Coulee Dam project. Sidney Garfield forms the SR Garfield MD and Associates medical group

1942

Henry J. Kaiser calls on Dr. Garfield to establish a health care plan for workers at a Kaiser steel mill in Fontana, the first step in establishing Kaiser Permanente's Southern California Region. Sidney Garfield forms the Sidney R. Garfield MD and Associates medical group

for on-the-job injuries, Garfield quickly saw that there was no place for the workers to be treated...no clinic...no hospital...nothing, for hundreds of miles.

Garfield and Morris decided to become partners and build a small hospital along the aqueduct route where they could provide an important service and make a profit for themselves and any investors. The plan called for Sidney to borrow $2,500 from his father as a down payment for an Indio contractor who agreed to build the 12-bed hospital for $50,000. Gene Morris would continue practicing in Indio and contribute from $300 to $400 a month toward start-up costs.

Garfield chose a site for the hospital about six miles east of the town of Desert Center along U.S. Highway 60. It was an excellent choice, near a work camp at one end of a six-mile tunnel system under construction. The work camp's contractor was so pleased to have Garfield's little hospital nearby for his workers that he offered to supply the hospital with water and electricity at no charge. Sidney demonstrated his business acumen by convincing several companies to sell him equipment and supplies with virtually no down payment, rather than forgo a sale in the tough Depression economy. Soon, he was able to furnish his hospital with the latest medical equipment, including an autoclave and X-ray machine, and even a General Electric air conditioner, quite an innovation.[11]

Contractors General Hospital opened its doors to patients in the fall of 1933. Drs. Garfield and Morris intended to offer traditional fee-for-service medical care for both on- and off-the-job injuries and illnesses.

LEFT & TOP
Aqueduct workers excavating one of a total of 92 miles of tunnels along the 242-mile aqueduct running from Lake Havasu behind Parker Dam

The fee-for-service concept might have worked fine. After all, there were many accidents on the construction project and many men in need of care. But as Sidney would later explain, the insurance carriers were not eager to pay his little clinic to provide it. "The insurance companies presumably had adequate funds," said Garfield, "but definitely did not want to pass them on to us. Half of our bills were rejected on the basis we had given too many treatments to their cases. Serious injuries ironically could have been our best source of revenue, but as soon as we had these patients in fair condition or out of shock, the carriers would spirit them away to

Los Angeles — 200 miles away — to their company doctors and hospitals. This action of the carriers, of course, diminished our income, but also wounded our professional pride. They were interfering with doctor-patient relationship, but there was nothing we could do about it — one of our first lessons in medical care — whoever pays the bills usually controls the services."[12]

Sidney Garfield's hospital was rapidly going broke. He warned his nurse, Betty Runyen, that he was running out of money to pay her. Garfield was also having trouble keeping up his payments to a surgical supply house and to the contractor who had built the hospital.

History of the Group Practice Movement

The group practice movement began in earnest in the early part of the 20th century. Many historians believe that the birth of the modern day group practice goes all the way back to the 1800s, when W. W. Mayo opened his first office in Rochester, Minnesota in 1864. The Mayo Clinic served as a catalyst for the formation of a number of other group practices in the Midwest, with six new Midwest groups established between 1900 and 1915 alone. Over the next 10 years, 106 new groups were established in the United States, 33 of them in the Midwest. Because of the Great Depression, group practice growth slowed to a crawl between 1926 and 1932, with only 17 new groups established throughout the country. After 1935, how-ever, the movement took off in earnest, with steady growth up to and beyond World War II. In most cases the single largest motivating factor for these early group practice pioneers was the desire to practice better medicine. An early 1950s survey conducted by the American Association of Medical Clinics (the original name of the American Medical Group Association) confirms this altruistic motive of early group practice pioneers: improving the quality of care was the most important reason cited for forming a group in the first place.

— *Quoted from American Medical Group Association web site*

Gene Morris asked to dissolve the partnership, forcing Sidney to buy him out, thus adding another drain on Garfield's disappearing resources.[13] The hospital might have closed if not for the intervention of the San Francisco-based Industrial Indemnity Exchange, the largest insurance carrier involved in the aqueduct project.

In what would turn out to be a very fortunate coincidence, the Industrial Indemnity Exchange was owned in part by the industrialist Henry J. Kaiser. Henry John Kaiser, who would have a profound influence on the delivery of health care in America, was born on May 9, 1882 in Sprout Brook, New York, the fourth child of Frank and Mary Kaiser. Henry quit school and went to work at odd jobs when he was 12 years old, perhaps driven as much by the family's need for additional income as his own restless energy. Kaiser was willing to do almost anything and landed a series of jobs, including retail clerk and salesman. By 1906, he owned and operated three photographic studios and supply stores on the Atlantic coast. Although the photography business was going well financially, Kaiser was losing interest and patience. "I couldn't do what people wanted in portrait photography. They all wanted to look like actors or actresses, not like themselves," he said.[14] Kaiser decided to give it up and head west.

In the summer of 1906, Henry Kaiser settled in Spokane, Washington. He applied for work at more than 100 places but, in a tight job market, failed to find a job. He finally approached a hardware store where he got the same message — no jobs; but by now, Henry was unwilling to take no for an answer. The hardware store had recently had a fire and Kaiser offered to clean and polish the damaged inventory which the store had given up for lost. Kaiser promptly hired a cadre of young women to clean the tarnished goods which the hardware store owners were then able to sell, much to their delight. So impressed with Kaiser's initiative and ingenuity, the store owners promptly hired Henry as their hardware salesman. In calling on contractors as part of his job, Kaiser became interested in the construction business so, in 1909, he left the hardware store and became a salesman for several gravel and cement companies. By 1914, he'd learned enough to go out on his own as a road building contractor under the banner of the Henry J. Kaiser Company, Limited. It was a very small start, just Henry and two employees, A.B. Ordway and Stewart McWhorter, but the Kaiser family of industries was born.

By the mid-1930s, Kaiser was certainly a wealthy man with many construction projects to his credit, but his great fortune and influence still lay ahead. In fact, it was during the 1940s, when Kaiser, then in his 60s, would launch many of the projects that elevated him to legendary status. Long before the Kaiser name became associated with health care, it dominated the worlds of business and industry. The Kaiser companies made steel

LEFT
Contractors General Hospital, six miles west of Desert Center along US Hwy 60. Betty Runyen, RN in front of the ambulance

MIDDLE
Sidney Garfield, MD outside Contractors General Hospital

RIGHT
Contractors General Hospital bank book, first quarter 1934

TOP
California registered historical landmark plaque, in downtown Desert Center

and cement and would help build our nation's great dams — Hoover, Bonneville and Grand Coulee. Henry Kaiser would build the ships that helped the U.S. and its allies win World War II. He built cars and housing developments. And when he couldn't find a decent hotel room in Hawaii, he personally supervised construction of the Hawaiian Village Hotel on Waikiki Beach.

Although Henry Kaiser would not be directly involved in Sidney Garfield's desert operation, he certainly saw the business benefit in keeping workers healthy. He sent the insurance company's chief planner, Harold Hatch, to take a look. Hatch saw great value in Garfield's hospital. The injured workers were getting good care on site and didn't have to be transported fifty to eighty miles across the desert to Indio or even further, into Los Angeles. Hatch knew that such trips often delayed treatment and even jeopardized survival. To help Garfield keep his hospital open, Hatch suggested a revolutionary method of operation: prepayment.

Industrial Indemnity agreed to pay Garfield 12.5 percent of the workers' compensation insurance premium, which amounted to $1.50 per worker per month, or 5 cents per day. Garfield then suggested that workers also be given the chance to voluntarily contribute another nickel per day out of their own paychecks for non-industrial coverage. According to Garfield, 95 percent of the men took him up on the comp coverage offer. The prepayment plan provided Garfield with $500 a day, plenty to keep his hospital open and running. Soon, Industrial Indemnity voluntarily upped the payment to Garfield to 17.5 percent, based on their satisfaction with the care he was providing and the fact that they no longer had to send patients to Los Angeles.

Garfield would later talk about the impact of prepayment on his practice: "To our amazement, this completely reversed our financial picture. From then on, we had a definite income each month, we could budget our expenses accordingly, were able to meet our payrolls

and started paying off our creditors. A really remarkable demonstration of the value of prepayment. Equally impressive, however, were two unexpected results of this arrangement. The first of these was a complete reversal in the attitude of the insurance carriers. Under this new arrangement — paying us a fixed amount of funds per month — they no longer cared how many times we treated their cases as long as we performed a satisfactory job; and, from that time on, they never moved a patient to Los Angeles unless we requested them to do so for some specialty service we couldn't provide. This simple arrangement placed medical care back in our hands where it belonged, which we greatly appreciated. The other unexpected result was a change in our attitude. When we were on fee-for-service, we had been anxious to have injured cases admitted to the hospital since that meant income and continued existence. Under this prepaid arrangement, we received the same amount of funds regardless, and we became anxious to keep these men uninjured. We became preventive accident conscious. We joined with the safety engineers in trying

to eliminate hazards on the job such as nail punctures and falling rocks in tunnels, and, as we did this preventive work which we enjoyed doing, we realized that under the fee-for-service system, we would have been rapidly eliminating our income and inevitably our services."[15]

Sidney Garfield and Ray Kay stayed in close contact throughout Sidney's years in the desert, from 1933 to 1938. "I would go out and visit him out there," remembered Kay. "We kept talking about all our desires [. . .] We were the closest of friends. I was interested in everything he did, and we were still talking about someday hoping to have an organization, you know, of being able to do something like we talked about."[16]

FAR LEFT
Aqueduct construction

MIDDLE
Ray Kay, MD visiting Contractors General Hospital

LEFT
Sidney Garfield, MD relaxes by target shooting from the front steps of his hospital

S.R. GARFIELD MD AND ASSOCIATES AND   THE GRAND COULEE DAM

When the aqueduct project was finished, Sidney Garfield
had every intention of returning to Los Angeles for more
surgical experience, but fate..and the Kaiser
organization…had something else in mind.

On a hot morning in July 1938, while Sidney
Garfield was still at Desert Center, he received a phone
call from A.B. Ordway, president of the Industrial
Indemnity Exchange.

"Kaiser just got the award for the Coulee Dam in
Washington," Ordway announced. "He heard about the
job you did for us down here, and he wants you to do
the medical job up there."[17] Garfield replied that he did
not want to take on another "temporary" job, but
wanted to get into private practice and put down some
roots. Ordway urged to him just to visit the Coulee
Dam site and meet with Henry Kaiser's son Edgar, one
of his father's key executives.

Sidney agreed to meet with Edgar Kaiser, but there
was no doubt in his mind that he would turn down the
Kaiser proposal. Then he saw the Grand Coulee Dam
site. This was going to be the biggest construction
project in the history of the world, bigger even than the
Great Pyramid of Egypt. Sidney Garfield was hooked.

Whereas workers on the desert aqueduct project had
been scattered over 500 square miles, at Coulee,
Garfield saw 5000 men all concentrated in one camp.
Several thousand more people, including the workers'

RUNNING COUNTER TO THE
FEE-FOR-SERVICE MODEL

Both prepayment and group medical practice [. . .] ran counter to the model of solo fee-for-service practice that the American medical community had determined to be the best model for medical practice in the United States. [. . .] Physicians in multi-specialty group practice, however, were quick to point out its advantages. Physicians in different specialties were available to each other for ready referrals. Sharing medical records created, automatically, a continuous de facto process of peer review. Group practice physicians were continually educating one another in the day-to-day practice of medicine. The sharing of hospital and clinic space; the consolidation of laboratory, X-ray, and other ancillary disciplines into one location; together with the unification of records keeping, billing, and other administrative procedures, all made for great efficiency and cost effectiveness. Despite these and other benefits, group practice, running as it did counter to the established model, remained a minor development in the early twentieth century. By 1932, a year before Sidney Garfield went out to the Mojave Desert, fewer than 2000 American physicians were in any form of group practice in the United States.

— *John G. Smillie, MD in his book,* Can Physicians Manage the Quality and Costs of Health Care? The Story of The Permanente Medical *Group, pp. 10–11.*

wives and children, lived in the community surrounding the camp. "I was completely intrigued by the scope of the work and the great need and opportunity for providing medical services," said Garfield.[18]

Garfield also saw Coulee as an opportunity to build a small medical group, SR Garfield MD and Associates. He started assembling a group of doctors, including his friend Wally Neighbor who had been practicing for five years at the Arrowhead Springs Resort in Southern California. "I was delighted," Neighbor remembered. "I was tired of taking care of the movie colony and the neurotics."[19] Sidney recruited Cecil Cutting, then a resident at San Francisco General Hospital. As evidence, even then, of the hostility towards Garfield's prepaid concept, Cecil Cutting's mentor, the Dean of the Stanford School of Medicine, warned him that going with Garfield would destroy a very promising career. Cutting, like so many pioneers of both the Northern and Southern California Permanente Medical Groups, would ignore the advice. Dr. Cutting would later become one of the seven original partners of The Permanente Medical Group in Northern California and the group's first Executive Director, a position he held from 1957 to 1976. Garfield asked Ray Kay to join his group as well, but, at the time, Kay was unable to leave his teaching commitments at USC and LA County Hospital.

SR Garfield MD and Associates worked out of a 75-bed hospital that Sidney had refurbished near the Grand Coulee Dam site. The workers were covered by the same kind of prepaid medical plan that had proven so successful in Garfield's desert hospital. But while the workers were covered, their families were not. Sidney Garfield had not confronted this problem in the desert where there were virtually no family members present. Here, there were thousands of women and children who could not afford to pay for medical care. The workers were very unhappy about the inequity. "Our doctors also became unhappy about this situation," said Garfield. "They were able to give everything needed in the way of medical care to the workers but when the wives or children of those workers were the patients, they were constantly being frustrated in securing necessary diagnostic studies and hospitalization because of this same inability to pay."[20]

The logical solution called for expanding the employee-only healthcare program into a true family health plan. Garfield and the Kaisers were definitely plowing new ground. "We sought advice all over the country but nobody could help us," recalled Garfield. "No one had a family plan that could act as a guide. Finally, we picked figures out of the air — 50 cents a week for the wife, 25 cents a week for the child [. . .] and we were soon taking care of women and children on a prepaid basis."[21]

When Sidney Garfield and Ray Kay had been at LA County Hospital, they had dreamed of medicine practiced without economic barriers. The Coulee Dam project would give Garfield a chance to see how their dream could work on a relatively large scale. He liked what he saw: "Prior to this family plan," said Garfield, "when walking through the corridors of our little hospital at Coulee, we would see very sick women and children. Some of them terminally ill with pneumonia, in oxygen tents; we saw them in the operating rooms with ruptured appendices, with mastoiditis, and even some cases of diphtheria. After the plan had been in operation for three or four months, there was a noticeable change in the severity level of illness. We no longer saw seriously ill women and children. Terminal pneumonias became early pneumonias, ruptured appendices became simple appendices; mastoiditis and diphtheria practically disappeared. The reason was simple. These people, with the barrier of cost for medical service removed, were coming to us early in their illness. We were able to treat them early, could prevent their becoming seriously sick, and actually prevent them from dying from neglected illness. This impressive result has been the basis of our deep conviction that a plan that places a barrier between the patient and his early approach to a doctor — such as one not covering the cost of the first two or three visits, or not covering the cost of illness until the patient is in the hospital — defeats its purpose and is not good."[22]

The Coulee experience not only solidified Garfield's belief in prepaid group medical practice, it also strengthened his respect for Henry J. Kaiser and his organization.

"We became closely acquainted with their high principles of operation and the objectives they had in

Cecil Cutting, MD outside of the Mason City Hospital at Grand Coulee Dam, circa 1938

common with us: the fulfillment of human needs," Garfield recalled. "In giving the best possible service to the people, we welded a common bond that grew stronger with each succeeding year. Mr. Kaiser, Sr. was intensely interested in our medical care program. He would quiz me about the plan for hours and with his usual scope of thinking, he immediately envisioned the medical profession spreading this plan throughout the entire country for the benefit of the people as well as the doctors."[23]

After the first few months, Sidney Garfield would spend only a day or two a month at the Grand Coulee site. He now turned his attention to Los Angeles where he'd accepted a teaching residency at LA County Hospital alongside Ray Kay. "So here Garfield and I were together again," said Kay, "and we started our thinking and dreaming all over again."[24]

America's entry into World War II would both interrupt and advance those dreams.

SAFETY FIRST

ABOVE
*Shift change at one of the
Kaiser WW II shipyards in
Richmond, California*

MIDDLE
*Several of the 1,490 ships
built by Kaiser during WW II
under construction*

RIGHT
*One of the several first aid
stations in the Richmond
shipyards*

GARFIELD, KAY AND THE PERMANENTE FOUNDATION

In 1942, both Sidney Garfield and Raymond Kay were part of a medical contingent from USC slated to be shipped to India. Shortly before they were set to leave, Sidney got another phone call from the Kaiser organization, this one from Clay Bedford, former chief engineer of the Grand Coulee project. "Mr. Bedford asked me to come up to Richmond to help them," Garfield later recounted. "He said they were having trouble getting the injured workers into the local hospitals, couldn't get doctors, and could I come up and help them. I told him I was in the Army and was supposed to embark for India in one month. He said, 'Well, you've got a month. Can you come up and advise me what to do.'"[25]

What the Kaiser organization wanted Sidney Garfield to do was set up a prepaid comprehensive medical program for the 30,000 workers at Henry J. Kaiser's shipbuilding facilities in Richmond, California. Like all of Kaiser's projects, it would be a massive undertaking, this time to build ships for America and her allies — and not just to build them, but to build them fast.

Shipbuilding was a critical wartime industry that relied on thousands of healthy workers and Henry Kaiser believed that Sidney Garfield was the only man with the experience and talent to run the Richmond medical program. Without Sidney's knowledge, Kaiser asked President Roosevelt to release Garfield from his military obligation so he could stay in Richmond. Roosevelt agreed that Dr. Garfield's contribution was vital to America's war effort and released Sidney from the Army. Sidney Garfield looked forward to the new challenge with one reservation, "loyalty to the physicians of his reserve unit, many of whom were his personal friends, especially Ray Kay."[26]

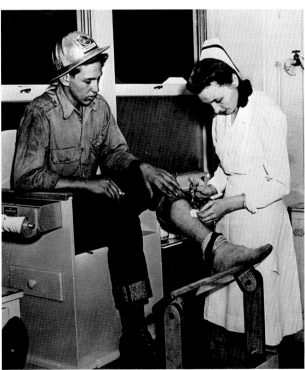

At first, Ray Kay was unhappy about Sidney's decision to remain in Richmond until the two men began talking things over and realized that the Richmond project "could form the cornerstone for establishing our statewide prepaid group practice when we all returned from the Army."[27] To accomplish this, Kay proposed that some health plan revenue be placed into a nonprofit foundation where it would be available to start new medical centers after the war. In later years, Sidney Garfield always gave Ray Kay credit for coming up with the concept of the nonprofit entities. Kay believed the idea was more the result of like-minded thinking. "It's really awfully difficult to say how an idea originated," recalled Kay. "My feeling is that this idea that he gives me credit for was actually a result of our reading and getting ideas from other organizations and the discussions that we had together, rather than the product of any one of our brains."[28]

Regardless of its genesis, both men believed the idea worth running by Henry Kaiser. "Sid took that idea to Mr. Henry Kaiser, Sr., and Mr. Kaiser thought it was a great idea," said Kay, "and we set up the Permanente Foundation as a nonprofit organization. The hospitals were turned over to that foundation, and Dr. Garfield would hire the doctors as Dr. Garfield and Associates, and he would pay the foundation for the hospital, and I think he was paying $20,000 a month. But if he had any extra money beyond that he would put that in and pay them thirty thousand or forty thousand, whatever he could pay them, every month. That was to build up this foundation which was to be used to build our facilities throughout California. [. . .] this was the beginning of our dream; this was the opportunity we'd been looking for."[29]

The name selected for the Foundation, "Permanente," was borrowed from the name of a creek running though the site of Henry J. Kaiser's cement factory about 40 miles south of San Francisco. In Spanish, the word

The Permanente Creek

permanente means permanent or everlasting, and both
Sidney Garfield and Henry Kaiser liked not just the
sound of the word, but its meaning.

Once established in 1942, the Permanente
Foundation became the umbrella under which Sidney
Garfield operated the hospitals, the health plan and the
medical group. "All physicians and staff were, in effect,
employees of Sidney Garfield. There was no separation
of management among the physician group, hospital
administration, and health plan. Every aspect of the
program came under the direct supervision of Garfield
or one of his designated physicians. In the words of
Cecil Cutting, the Permanente program was "a single
ball of wax."[30] It would remain so until February 1948
when the medical care program was restructured into
three separate entities: the Permanente Health Plan,
Permanente Hospitals and The Permanente Medical
Group, a partnership of physicians in Northern
California and later to include similar partnerships in
other regions. That basic organizational structure
endures to the present day.

While Sidney Garfield worked during World War II
to build up the new Permanente Foundation, Ray Kay
served in the military where he promoted the idea of
group practice, perhaps anticipating the day when he'd
be recruiting physicians for a group of his own. "So
when Garfield was doing this, I was in the army for over
five and a half years," said Kay. "And during my years
in the army I was constantly looking for and talking to
doctors about the possibility of working in groups on a
prepayment basis. [. . .] I found that during these years
in the army when we sat waiting to be sent overseas or
were coming home that most of the young doctors that
now were pulled up from practice and had no economic
ties were as interested as I was in working on a prepaid
basis, with no economic blocks, in a group of doctors
where they could develop together. A lot of them
wanted to do this when they came back from the army,
but there was no place for them to go. So they went
back into private practice on a fee-for-service basis."[31]

Ray Kay also had the chance to practice on a fee-for-
service basis after he ended his military duty in 1946,
but preferred to take a full-time job with the University

of Southern California and the Los Angeles County
Hospital teaching students and developing a residency
program for returning doctors. As he recalled, "We
trained about a hundred and fifty residents at a time.
[. . .] Later, I got a lot of my Permanente doctors from
there. But it was fun, and I enjoyed it, and I learned a
lot, and this was what I was doing. As I was doing it I
would develop good friendships with my students and
my people, and I was playing with this prepaid medicine
idea. I sent Dr. Alvin Sanborn when he finished his
residency out to be head of the Kaiser company hospital
at Fontana."[32] [The Fontana hospital had opened in

1943 at the site of the then-new Kaiser Steel Mill; Dr. Sanborn started there in 1946.]

Ray Kay himself would go to Fontana in 1949 at Garfield's request. Together again, Garfield and Kay would start realizing the dreams they'd had at LA County more than 15 years before, of establishing "a form of practice that we hoped would meet the needs of both patients and physician."[33] Part of their dream was to transform Sidney R. Garfield and Associates into the Southern California Permanente Medical Group. It would take a few more years, but the wheels of change were in motion.

LEFT
*Lt. Colonel and Mrs. Raymond Kay
with infant daughter, Karen, circa 1943*

TOP
Lt. Colonel Raymond Kay

RAY KAY…
IN TUNE WITH THE TIMES

The thinking that gave rise to our medical care program began in an era very different from the present one. In the 1930s, when [Dr. Garfield] and I were in training, there were no social services, no Medicare or Medicaid, no health insurance, and certainly there were no HMOs. When people became ill or needed medical care, they had two options: expensive private practice or the county hospital. It seems that we were at a point of social change, where the Great Depression and the innovative policies of the Roosevelt Administration began to emphasize the need to help those who could not help themselves. So the thinking and actions of Dr. Garfield and myself were a product of the times and really represented the feelings and the desires of many young doctors of our age.

— *Raymond Kay, MD, speaking in 1984*

"A Moment in Time"

*Remembering Betty Runyen:
How Sidney Garfield's First Nurse
Helped Mold the Principles of
Permanente Medicine*

By Steve Gilford

In the fall of 1933, a young Dr. Sidney Garfield and his friend and partner, Dr. Gene Morris, had just taken a big chance. In the middle of the Depression, they opened a small hospital at a remote construction site in the Southern California desert.

Garfield and Morris had set out to meet the medical needs of 5000 Colorado River Aqueduct construction workers digging a man-made river across the desert and through mountains to connect the thirsty Los Angeles with the abundant water of the Colorado River more than two hundred miles away.

Gene Morris was already in practice in Indio, the nearest town of any size. As part of his contribution to the hospital start-up, he promised Sidney Garfield that he would find and hire a suitable local nurse for their hospital. The name on the top of his list was 21-year-old Betty Runyen. Occasionally, she worked for him when his regular nurse needed time off for illness or vacation. He'd been impressed with both her professionalism and her charm. Betty had another advantage — she'd grown up in the area. Desert weather would be familiar to her.

Reached by phone in Los Angeles, where she was working at Methodist Hospital, Betty was excited by Gene Morris' offer of a full-time job at Contractors General Hospital. He said she would be working for his partner, Sidney Garfield, in what he described as the rough conditions of a desert construction camp — a challenge that appealed to Betty's adventurous spirit. Two days later, she reported for work at Contractors General Hospital. It was the day she met Sidney Garfield.

Clearly, Garfield was glad to see her. In addition to being the only physician, he'd been trying to handle the nursing chores too. He needed help.

Playing the good host, Garfield eagerly showed Miss Runyen around the hospital he had financed, designed, and helped build. It consisted of 12 patient beds — ten beds in a ward and two beds in a semiprivate room — plus an exam room, a well-equipped OR, and a few rooms for the live-in physician and staff, including a married couple who were the hospital's orderly, ambulance driver, and housekeeping team. There was also a kitchen, a laundry, and a tiny bedroom for Betty. All of this was packed into a 2000-square-foot wood-frame building, set down among cactus and cholla bushes, on the edge of a construction camp about six miles west of the aptly named town of Desert Center. This little oasis of healing — the only hospital in the area — was to be Betty's home for the next five years.

Before long, Betty adjusted to the pace of life and work at Contractors General. Most mornings, she stayed in bed until she heard the orderly and his wife in the kitchen preparing breakfast. Then, she'd knock on Sidney Garfield's door to wake him. Garfield slept in the combination office and apartment just inside the hospital's front door. This area was where the staff met for breakfast every morning. While Garfield took his morning shower, the orderly set up breakfast on a folding card table.

There were no special dispensary hours for the aqueduct workers. They would

Betty Runyen, RN presents safety trophy hard hat to an Aqueduct Construction Supervisor for his crews' safety record.

just walk in the back door, go to the Treatment Room, and wait for someone. They didn't have to wait long because Betty Runyen or Sidney Garfield would have heard the screen door slam and gone to help them. Broken arms, legs, and fingers were fairly common, as were back injuries. Another common malady was "Powder Headache": It was caused by getting a little too close to dynamite explosions, especially in the miles of hard-rock tunnels where they were blasting through mountain ranges to complete the aqueduct.

Although Betty often doubled as an ambulance driver, only once did she go out to pick up a patient by herself. It happened on an afternoon when Sidney Garfield was in Indio, leaving Betty Runyen as the only medical person at the hospital. She was dreading that an emergency call might come in, and that is exactly what happened. A worker at a nearby construction camp had fainted from the heat.

When Betty reached the patient, she started an IV of normal saline for him, and the patient immediately began recovering. This procedure may seem routine today, but in 1933, nurses didn't start IVs; that was solely a function of the physician. However, it was typical of Sidney Garfield that he had trained her to act in just this sort of emergency. 40-years later, when Nurse Practitioner training was introduced in Kaiser Permanente, Garfield, along with the enthusiastic cooperation of a group of Permanente physicians, helped the Medical Care Program demonstrate nationally that the Nurse Practitioner

could be an important part of the health care delivery team.

In addition to satisfying her taste for adventure, the desert years with Sidney Garfield gave Betty Runyen an opportunity to experience firsthand some milestone events in health care history. She recalled that after nearly a year of struggling with underwriters to get full payment for treatment they were providing, Sidney Garfield was running out of money. One day, she said, he did something very unusual: He invited her to join him for a glass of wine — in fact, for a couple of glasses. He had something unpleasant to say, but first he had to loosen up a little.

When he was ready, he told Betty that he was not going to be able to meet the next payroll. Then he blurted out, "I've got to cut your salary, and if you don't like it, you can quit." Coming straight out like that, it sounded almost like an ultimatum, but she understood that his curtness came out of his disappointment and embarrassment.

Betty was shocked and surprised; but when Garfield explained the problem, she and the housekeeping couple volunteered to work without pay until the hospital became more financially stable. During the next few months, with the help of Harold Hatch, an executive with an insurance company partially

owned by Henry J. Kaiser, the still-revolutionary concept of prepayment was introduced at Contractors General, covering up to 5000 workers. Within months, the hospital was on its way to becoming a financial success, and Betty and her co-workers received their back pay.

Sidney Garfield and Betty Runyen thus were among the first to see how prepayment could change the whole economics of medical practice — a subject that Garfield would promote for the rest of his life. Soon, with the proper incentive in place, Sidney Garfield and Betty Runyen were out in the work camps, promoting the proper use of salt tablets, encouraging preventive care — safely shoring up tunnels, banging down nails, and reminding the men of the importance of wearing hard hats and keeping the workplace clear of dangerous, discarded objects. With Betty Runyen's help, the principles of what would become Permanente Medicine were being hammered into the historical record.

(8) Partnership has the right to continue its business on the death, retirement or insanity of a general partner.

CHAPTER TWO

Raymond M. Kay, M.D.

Frederick H. Scharles, M.D.

Alvin L. Sanborn, M.D.

Herman Weiner, M.D.

Jack Hallatt, M.D.

John H. Winkley, M.D.

Leonard S. Buck, M.D.

Charles W. Knerler, M.D.

Erwin D. Goldenberg, M.D.

Roy Miranda, M.D.

Irving Klitsner, M.D.

Edward A. Loeb, M.D.

Rene Cailliet, M.D.

Subscribed and sworn to before me

this 22ⁿᵈ day of December, 1952

Notary Public in and for the County of Los Angeles, State of California. My Commission Expires Apr. 3,
(Seal)   1956

3.

BUILDING THE DREAM

"Sid and I had dreamed of partnerships all the way through. But I didn't want it until I had a good group because I didn't want any poor partners."

— *Ray Kay, MD*

B Y the mid-1940s, Sidney Garfield had already headed up several small groups of physicians working for him as employees. But both Garfield and Ray Kay believed that physicians should not "work for anyone" — even Sidney Garfield. They believed that physicians should have their own organization…a partnership. In Southern California, the transition of physicians from employees to partners — from Sidney R. Garfield, MD and Associates to the Southern California Permanente Medical Group — would begin in Fontana, primarily under Ray Kay's leadership.

FONTANA AND THE MEDICAL GROUP'S FIRST YEARS

The Fontana operation began in 1942, as part of Henry J. Kaiser's initial foray into Southern California. He came at first, not to provide health care, but to build a new steel mill to supply the voracious needs of his shipbuilding industries.

Kaiser purchased a huge parcel of land for his steel mill, in an area of pig ranches and fruit orchards. Fontana was selected for its strategic location — far enough inland to be safe from an attack on the West Coast and located on two railroad lines connecting it with other Kaiser facilities in Utah and California. So urgent was Henry Kaiser's need for steel, that he was determined to build the new steel mill as quickly as possible. Construction began in April of 1942 and

Kaiser promised he would have a blast furnace in operation by New Year's Day. "No one had ever built a steel plant that fast and Kaiser had the additional handicap of wartime shortages of some of the materials he had to have to build his plant," noted Steve Gilford in his article about the steel mill's early days. "It was hard to find anyone in the steel business, except Kaiser and his crews, who thought the Kaiser schedule was anywhere possible."[1] But Kaiser did it — he wasn't nicknamed "Hurry-Up Henry" for nothing. On December 30 — one day ahead of schedule — Henry Kaiser's wife Bess threw the switch to light the plant's first blast furnace. Kaiser had named the 10-story, 1200-ton blast furnace "Bess" in honor of his wife. A few months later, the plant's rolling mill was completed and began turning out steel plates for the hulls of the Liberty ships, Victory ships, troop carriers, aircraft carriers and oil tankers so vital to America's war effort.

As had been the case in other newly-launched Kaiser industrial enterprises, the steel plant did not have adequate health care for its 3000 workers, so Henry Kaiser again called on Sidney Garfield to help. Garfield was already overwhelmed with work in the shipyards and not eager to launch yet another project. "But it [. . .] gave me an opportunity," he would say, "to get my foothold in the south. I remembered my commitment to Ray Kay that eventually I would have a plan in Los Angeles."[2]

When Garfield arrived in Fontana, one of his first moves was to convert the mill's administration building into a 50-bed hospital. The project was begun in March 1943 and completed just three months later, as noted with pride in the company newspaper, *The Snorter*. "Now our hospital is about to open, offering employees and families of Kaiser company medical and hospital care for less than the cost of a

FAR LEFT
Souvenir paperweight made from the first pig iron produced at the Fontana plant

BACKGROUND AND RIGHT
Kaiser's Fontana Steel Mill looking east. The four blast furnaces are at the left. On the right are the stacks for nine open-hearth furnaces

A PAPER BY AND ABOUT KAISER CO. EMPLOYEES

VOL. 1—No. 36   FONTANA, CALIFORNIA   FRIDAY, SEPTEMBER 3, 1943

It's Here! Your Health Protection Plan

DEDICATED TO KEEPING YOU WELL—These are the doors through which employes of Kaiser Company will pass whenever seeking relief from sickness or injury. Behind these doors will be found one of the most modern, completely equipped hospitals of this area . . . and its yours . . . the workers and families of the steel mill . . . yours for less than the price of a dish of ice cream per day. This hospital is interested in keeping you well. Use its services for smallest injury or slightest sickness.

Snorty is one of the happiest little guys at the steel mill this week, because at last he is able to announce the opening of the new field hospital to all the workers and their families at the steel mill and to tell them, that at last, they can have adequate medical care and still not go broke.

Death and taxes are the two things no man can escape, according to the old adage . . . but there is sickness, too. There are a few fortunate people who go through life without the pain and expense of even a single long illness, but industrial statistics, insurance records and probably even your own personal experiences all point to the too frequent instances where the savings of a lifetime, the future earnings, the economical life of a great many working families, are wiped out by the unexpected . . . illness.

Because this need never happen again in the lives of Kaiser employes, Snorty is happy, for this week he can tell you all about the new health plan and the opening of the Southern Permanente hospital . . . our own hospital directly behind the administration building.

This is the story of health protection, a story of the hospital, of the health plan, the doctors, nurses and technicians who will remove the waste of sickness from those of us who work here at the steel mill.

But to really start the story at the beginning, we have to go back several years to the time when the All-American Canal was being built through the Imperial Valley, for it was on this project that a young doctor, Sidney Garfield, was trying to care for the medical needs of the workmen. He was faced with the problem of caring for the men who were sick and injured, but without proper facilities. The nearest town for hospital treatment was miles away . . . too far to be of any use. By tirelessly plugging, Dr. Garfield finally managed to have a small hospital built out in the hot desert near Desert Center.

Shortly after that, Kaiser company was working on the Coulee Dam project . . . again a project employing thousands of men but too far away from a town to give the men hospital care when they were sick or injured. With this need staring them in the face, a modern hospital was built near the dam, and Dr. Garfield was called in to operate it on a plan similar to that we are starting at the steel mill this week . . . That was the birth of our hospital plan. When the project was completed, the government took over the operation of the hospital and is operating it today for the men and women of that wild area of Washington State, far from any metropolitan medical service.

Then came the shipyards, and the Kaiser company again began hiring large numbers of men and women. There were not enough hospital and medical facilities in Richmond and Vancouver to care for this increasing need and again the Kaiser company built hospitals at Vancouver and Oakland, calling in Dr. Garfield to operate them.

Now our hospital is about to open, offering employes and families of Kaiser company medical and hospital care for less than the cost of a dish of ice cream per day.

It hasn't been easy to build our hospital, equip it, staff it and make it ready

(Continued on page six)

Snorty Invites You

Our new hospital is going to hold an open house next Sunday afternoon, and Snorty wants to invite every employe and his family to be there to inspect this modern hospital which will be serving your medical needs for years to come.

The open house will start at 2 p. m. and continue until 8 p. m. and Snorty would like to see everyone here at the steel mill drop by some time during those hours to inspect this new building. For those who may not know, the hospital is directly behind the administration building, just north of the parking lot.

dish of ice cream per day. It hasn't been easy to build our hospital, equip it, staff it and make it ready for our use. Under war-time conditions, the building of our hospital has been nothing but a battle of priorities. All those materials that go into a modern hospital have become as rare as hen's teeth."[3]

The hospital admitted its first patient, a Kaiser steel mill employee, on July 15, 1943. Patient #0000041 was treated under the Workmens Compensation program which required the employer to provide care for workers injured on the job. A few months later, on September 13, 1943, the Health Plan went into effect which would provide comprehensive care for workers, covering non-work-related illness or injury. The Health Plan was offered to all Kaiser steel mill employees on a voluntary basis; 60 cents a week for an adult and 30 cents per week per child. Non-members could also be treated at the hospital for $9 per day for a private room and $7 for a ward bed. For non-members, chest X-rays cost $10 and skull X-rays cost between $15 and $25. Blood counts and EKGs were done for $5 each. Non-members paid $5 for their first clinic visit, with follow-up visits for the same ailment costing just $2.50.[4] In 1945, Garfield and his group would open the Health Plan to the residents of Fontana and surrounding communities.

The Fontana hospital opened with a staff of six physicians, all employed by Sidney Garfield as part of his small medical group, Sidney R. Garfield, MD and Associates. The six included Drs. Mar McGregor (Physician-in-Charge and surgeon); Ed Loeb (pediatrician); Virgil Snow (general practitioner); Jules Cloud (surgeon); Bill Hunt (ENT); and Roy Miranda (OB/GYN). Alvin Sanborn joined the group as the Chief of Internal Medicine in 1946. A year later, he would be appointed Medical Director of the Fontana facility.

Once Ray Kay had returned from the Army and started working in Los Angeles, Garfield would often talk with him and ask his advice, especially about administrative problems in Fontana. One such problem arose in 1949 when Dr. Jules Plaut, a Fontana surgeon, began claiming that the other physicians were not practicing "good medicine." Furthermore, he complained that Sidney Garfield was gone most of the

time and that Alvin Sanborn didn't have the authority he needed to take over in Garfield's absence. Plaut won Bill Brunton, the steelworkers' union president, over to his side of the issue and soon, Brunton was pushing to remove Garfield and Sanborn from Fontana and replace them with Jules Plaut.

Sidney Garfield asked Ray Kay to join him in the many meetings that the physicians, management and the union were having in Fontana about this and other issues, at first, more to listen and learn than participate. "Well, as they went on I got into more and more of the meetings," said Ray Kay. "At the end of them Sid Garfield asked me if I would go down to Fontana, not as medical director to replace Sanborn, which I would not do, but to go down to be his representative, and that anything that I said should be done would be done. So I did."[5]

Ray Kay left his job at LA County Hospital in 1949, moved to Fontana and joined the organization as Medical Director of the Southern California Region. It would be one of the defining moments in SCPMG's history. Within a few years, Ray Kay would be the driving force in transforming a little medical group owned by Sidney Garfield into the partnership of physicians known as the Southern California Permanente Medical Group. Kay's commitment to SCPMG and his passion for prepaid group practice would sustain the Medical Group through crises and conflicts that might have destroyed it in less capable hands. Kay would truly prove to be the right man for the job ahead.

FAR LEFT
The workers' weekly newsletter, "The Snorter, by and about Kaiser Co. employees," announces the opening of the Health Protection Plan. The first words of the article are "Dedicated to keeping you well," a clear statement of preventive medicine.
September 1943

ESTABLISHING THE MEDICAL GROUP'S CORE PRINCIPLES

Although SCPMG would not be officially formed until 1953, Ray Kay and the small medical group in Fontana began establishing many core principles that remain at the heart of SCPMG today. Many of these principles evolved out of a particular challenge or crisis whose solution helped the group define itself and its new type of practice.

One of the first principles established grew out of a battle with the union over the retention of an optometrist who, in Kay's opinion, "was no good." The union head, Bill Brunton, insisted that the group retain the man regardless of what Kay or any other physician wanted. In later years, Kay would take great delight in relating his exchange with Brunton. "So I told Bill Brunton," said Kay, "'He'll have to go.' And Bill Brunton says, 'Oh, no you won't.' And he says, 'He's going to stay in here.' And I said, 'Well, he isn't.' And we argued for quite a while. And he says, 'Doc, this is one I'm going to win because I'll go to Mr. Kaiser on this.' And I said, 'Well, Bill, if you go to Mr. Kaiser and he interferes, all of our doctors will walk out.' 'Oh,' he says, 'So you're going to strike on me, huh?' I said, 'It's that important to us. We cannot have anybody interfering with our medical care.'"[6]

Kay won the battle, but more important, he established "the one principle in which there could be no compromise: medical care must be the responsibility of the physicians and their medical group."[7] That principle would spark some bitter battles in coming years, but the group would hold firm on its insistence that physicians, and no one else, control the practice of medicine.

KAISER STEEL MILL FONTANA CAL

Another principle grew out of Kay's commitment to deliver the best medical care possible to Health Plan members. While he was happy with the care provided by the full-time physicians Garfield had hired, he was very unhappy with many of the local physicians and residents they had hired to work nights and weekends. "I therefore decided that we had to get rid of them [the non-Garfield doctors]," said Kay, "and that we [Garfield's group] had to take turns doing the night duty. In other words we had to have our good regular doctors there to see people at all times. So Dr. Sanborn and I decided that we were going to dispense with [. . .] these men from outside, and the staff was going to take turns doing night duty and walk-ins. Well, about half of the guys said they wouldn't do it. So we said, 'Okay, find another job.'"[8]

As Kay would often say, it was another lesson learned: "That the practice of any physician in the group represented all of us and that we cannot allow physicians of questionable caliber to care for our patients."[9]

Fontana also proved the wisdom of integrating family physicians within a multispecialty group setting. As Ray Kay noted in his book, "the Northern California Medical Group did not believe in using family physicians because they felt that they were not of the same professional caliber as the specialists."[10] But in Fontana, Dr. Dean McCandless, a family practitioner, convinced the group that competent, well-trained family physicians could be a positive addition, and that was found to be true. "The Family Practice Service that he developed," said Kay, "added flexibility to the staff and improved our care. The value of a department of Family Practice has led to the establishment of similar departments at most of our medical centers."[11]

BUILDING UP FONTANA

Throughout the late 1940s, the Medical Group in Fontana continued to operate as Sidney R. Garfield, MD and Associates with the understanding that Garfield would transfer his ownership to the group when the group was ready. "Sid and I had dreamed of partnerships all the way through," said Kay. "But I didn't want it until I had a good group because I didn't want any poor partners. I didn't have that many good doctors at Fontana."[12]

Ray Kay made a concerted effort to build up the staff in Fontana in preparation for an eventual partnership, bringing on full-time, well-trained physicians who were dedicated to the prepaid group practice concept. As Fontana continued to grow, the Medical Group also geared up for a major move to Harbor City and a step closer to forming its official partnership.

LEFT
First Hospital at Kaiser Steel Mill in Fontana,
made from a converted administration building

RIGHT
Alvin Sanborn, MD

FEBRUARY 9, 1950

On this date, the entire International Longshoremen and Warehousemen Union (ILWU), nearly six thousand workers spread out along the West Coast from Washington to Southern California, plus their families, were enrolled in the Permanente Health Plan. The choice of health care coverage was made by the ILWU's president, the charismatic and highly controversial Harry Bridges, who had been attracted by the comprehensive coverage offered by the Health Plan. The Plan, still recovering from the postwar slump in membership, was delighted to have this influx of new members.

Bridges, one of the major figures of West Coast labor history, required that Garfield be able to treat his union members in ports all along the Pacific Coast. As a result, the Health Plan had to move, immediately, into the Los Angeles area. Until this time, the only Health Plan facility in the region was at the steel plant in Fontana. The move into San Pedro represented the real beginning of the Southern California Region. It certainly was a modest start; rented space on the first floor of a building at the corner of Ninth and Grand in the port of San Pedro.

Harry Bridges' decision forced his men to leave what, in some cases, had been long-time relationships with their family physicians. Not surprisingly, there was a great deal of resentment towards the Permanente doctors. To reduce tensions and to help physicians understand the working environment of the Longshoremen, union officials set up visits to the docks for the Permanente doctors, where the physicians learned about their life, their dangers, even their vocabulary. In a rough-hewn sort of way, it probably was one of the Program's first examples of cultural sensitivity training. Ira "Buck" Wallin, the first physician to be assigned by Ray Kay to the San Pedro facility, remembered these longshoremen as being particularly tough individuals. In fact, one of the physicians, Leon Quattelbaum, was killed in a bar when he was punched in the stomach by a longshoreman. Dr Wallin said of that period,

"It was not unusual for them to come into the office still carrying their mean-looking cargo hooks. This was somewhat intimidating for the physicians who treated them, especially if the longshoremen were already upset that they had been forced to leave their regular physician due to union president Harry Bridges having selected their health care provider for them."

He did add that there was an upside to the relationship, too:

"If a longshoreman was pleased with his medical care, he might show up at an appointment with a gift for the doctor that came from a 'damaged crate' on the dock. The doctor would be presented with a watch or perfume, something small but of value."

— *Steve Gilford, On This Date in KP History*

THE MEDICAL GROUP EXPANDS TO HARBOR CITY

The Medical Group's move to Harbor City was initiated in 1950 by Harry Bridges, president of the International Longshoremen and Warehousemen Union. Bridges had approached Sidney Garfield asking that the Permanente Health Plan be provided for all his union members on the Pacific Coast, from Seattle to San Diego.

At the time, the Permanente Health Plan was not offered in the metropolitan Los Angeles area, nor was Henry Kaiser particularly interested in expanding to Southern California. "You know," said Garfield, "San Franciscans don't like Los Angeles. I would talk to them and work on them every time I saw them and I was getting no place fast. They weren't interested in the Los Angeles area."[13] But once the ILWU contract was signed, the argument ended. Permanente would come to LA.

While Sidney Garfield was wondering just how he'd accomplish the Southland expansion, Dr. Ira ("Buck") Wallin was being interviewed by Ray Kay for a job in Fontana. "They were offering $500 a month," recalled Wallin. "Now, it was real money. And so I went to work out there as a Locum Tenens, which means my job was a temporary location."[14] Wallin got the Fontana job in October 1950. He described what happened next, just a couple weeks after he'd started working: "Sidney Garfield blew in. That's a very accurate description, 'blew in.' He talked to Ray for a while and then Ray called me and said, 'I want to talk with some of my men later. Why don't you hang around?'" Wallin did. Garfield had apparently asked Ray Kay to set up a medical care program in the harbor area, and so Kay looked to his Fontana physicians for help. Suddenly Kay turned to Wallin. "You're single?" he asked. When Wallin replied in the affirmative, Kay asked, "How would you like to do Locum Tenens down by the beach?" "I'll take a look at it," replied Wallin.

The next day Kay and Wallin drove to San Pedro. "Instead of going to a beach, we were driving through myriads of oil wells in San Pedro. I said, 'Ray, where is the beach? Are you conning me?' 'No, no, no. There really is a beach down by the foot of San Pedro,' replied Kay. He also said, 'I've got a list here of three or four places that we could get a rental going and set you up as a doctor.' I thought, 'this guy moves fast!'" "Do I have this right?" interviewer Steve Gilford asked Wallin. "You'd joined this Group about a week before and now you're being sent to start a new location and to be Physician-in-Charge at the new clinic?" "That's right," answered Wallin.

About two weeks later, Buck Wallin started work in San Pedro in medical offices leased by The Permanente Foundation. The Medical Group, still operating as Sidney R. Garfield, MD and Associates, had signed contracts with three physicians in the building, a pediatrician, a surgeon and an internist who were to work with the Group in caring for the union membership. And that was the San Pedro start-up staff, Wallin and three non-Group physicians. While hiring "outside" physicians may seem to have gone against Ray Kay's recently-established principle that the Group would not use part-timers, that principle was

1949

Raymond Kay appointed the first Medical Director of Kaiser Permanente Southern California Region

1950

The entire membership of the International Longshoremen and Warehousemen Union enrolls in the Permanente Health Plan; Sidney R. Garfield, MD and Associates establish their group in San Pedro to care for ILWU workers

1951

Program expands to Los Angeles to serve Retail Clerks Union

1953

Southern California Permanente Medical Group forms as a partnership, with Dr. Raymond Kay as Regional Medical Director

temporarily overridden by another Kay principle — always do what you need to do to meet the needs of the members. Of necessity, Kay also made arrangements with a local hospital to admit Permanente Health Plan patients.

The arrival of the Health Plan and Medical Group in San Pedro caused the established fee-for-service physicians to kick up some serious opposition to the encroachment of a prepaid plan on their territory. The Garfield physicians in Fontana had already experienced a less-than-warm reception from the local medical community, especially after offering the Health Plan beyond the boundaries of the Kaiser steel mill. The Fontana physicians had been denied membership in local medical societies and were not allowed to practice in the area hospitals. The opposition in the harbor area was even more intense and overt.

"Well, believe it or not," said Wallin, "this thing came apart almost as fast as it went together." Soon, the local physicians who had agreed to work with the Medical Group backed out of their commitments. "So here I am," said Wallin, "and I said to one of the doctors at the clinic, 'Would you take a look at this patient?' He tells me, 'I'm sorry, I'm going to be moving out, I want to get my own office practice going.' My opinion was that they were under pressure from the Los Angeles County Medical Society not to cooperate with us. Pretty soon the second outside doctor in our office goes and then the third. [. . .] We had three specialists who had agreed to see patients. We had shaken hands on it. It turned out it wasn't worth anything." "How long did it take the LA Medical Society to get these doctors to dissociate themselves from Sidney Garfield and Associates?" asked Gilford. Replied Wallin: "Probably three to six months."

Ray Kay, recalling that period, said, "All doctors were against us. [. . .] Some people were saying it was socialized medicine. Some would say we were working for Mr. Kaiser. Some were just scared it was going to affect their practice. In other words they'd all have different reasons for being against us. But they were all against us."[15] Even Wallin's friends turned on him. "I had a medical residency classmate, Meyer," Wallin recalled. "It happened that his office was right across the street. I thought it was great. I got permission to give him three or four people per week, whatever Ray and Sid decided, for consults in dermatology. The morning after I sent him the first one, he called me. 'Buck, I gotta

take it all back.' 'What's the matter? I'll make sure you get your money.' 'No, that is not it.' I suggested that we have lunch. 'Okay, but I've got to have it downtown. I don't want to be seen with you.' This was my old friend Meyer talking. At this time, I was kind of feisty myself. I said, 'The hell with you.'"

The Medical Group would continue to use local hospitals until their own Harbor City Medical Center was completed in 1957, but the message was clear —

the Permanente Foundation needed its own facilities and its own physicians. And not just any physicians. According to Ray Kay, he would need "a medical staff whose sole interest was our Medical Group and our type of medicine. Our experience [. . .] also convinced us that the most important element in forming a group of physicians is a stable core of dedicated doctors."[16]

With Fontana and now Harbor City, Ray Kay was slowly building his "stable core" of physicians...and not a moment too soon. Health Plan enrollment was just about to explode.

LEFT
Harbor City Medical Center,
about 1957

TOP
Ground-breaking ceremony for
Harbor City Medical Center

The Appeal of Group Practice

Group practice does not appeal to everyone and not everyone is suited to group practice, but if one becomes an accepted elected partner he has security professionally and economically and is a member of a medical care team of which he can be proud.

— *Jack Hallatt, MD, one of SCPMG's first senior partners*

Henry J. Kaiser on Group Practice

Today, with the need for more and more specialization, it is even more necessary for doctors to share their knowledge and skills — to pool them — if they are to give their patients the best, comprehensive medical care. It is the clinical way to modern medicine.

— *Henry J. Kaiser speaking to the National Press Club in Washington, D.C., May 26, 1954*

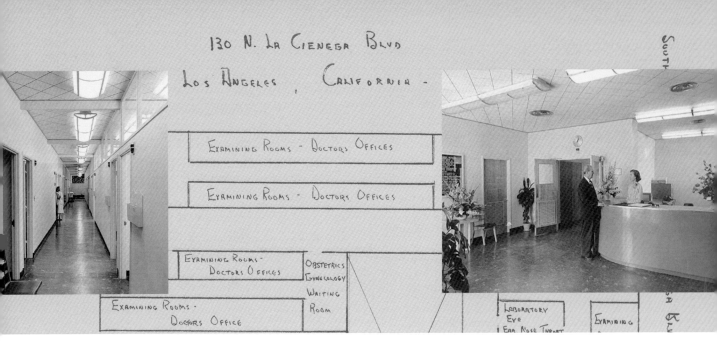

130 N. La Cienega Blvd
Los Angeles, California -

South

EXAMINING ROOMS - DOCTORS OFFICES

EXAMINING ROOMS - DOCTORS OFFICES

EXAMINING ROOMS - DOCTORS OFFICES

OBSTETRICS GYNECOLOGY WAITING ROOM

EXAMINING ROOMS - DOCTORS OFFICE

LABORATORY EYE EAR NOSE THROAT

EXAMINING

COMING TO LOS ANGELES

Within seven months of moving into the harbor area, Sidney Garfield received another of his life-altering phone calls, this one from Joe De Silva, head of the Retail Clerks Union Local 770, in Los Angeles. De Silva, an unusually farsighted man, wanted to provide medical care for his 25,000 union workers and had put together a task force to study the best way to do it. The task force had recommended the Permanente plan and hence the call to Garfield. "Let's get this going in LA," De Silva told Garfield. Still, a few of De Silva's advisors cautioned him about proceeding. "De Silva's advisors told him he was taking a big chance," recalled Dr. Ray Marcus, one of the first physicians to be hired in Los Angeles. "They said there were no buildings, there was no clinic, it's just talk."[17] But De Silva looked beyond the temporary lack of facilities. He had confidence in the Permanente plan. He'd met Ray Kay and appreciated his commitment to quality of care. He was eager to get started. According to Ray Marcus, De Silva presented the Group with a check for $90,000 — three months dues in advance — to start building medical offices in the Rexall Building on La Cienega Boulevard in Los Angeles.

Ray Marcus had been hired even before the La Cienega office opened in April 1951. The office was staffed by sixteen physicians, with Dr. Ray Kay as Medical Director. Initially, the 25,000 members of the Retail Clerks Union were all cared for at the single La Cienega clinic by the sixteen physicians. In addition to

Dr. Marcus, the original sixteen included Drs. Irv Klitsner and Erwin Goldenberg who served as co-Chiefs of Pediatrics. Dr. Jack Hallatt was Chief of OB/GYN and its only practitioner. Drs. Herman Weiner and Fred Scharles served as Ray Kay's Associate Medical Directors and practiced as well. Even Dr. Kay saw patients about once a week.

At the time, of course, the Medical Group did not have its own hospital in Los Angeles, so had to lease beds "all over town," as Ray Kay would often say. It was not a particularly happy arrangement. Irv Klitsner, for one, resisted admitting his pediatric patients to some of the hospitals the Group was being forced to use, believing that the quality of care was not up to the Group's standards. "It was tough admitting our patients to some of these small hospitals," he recalled, "because the nursing care was not real competent. A lot of them didn't know how to take care of little kids. There was a small hospital right near La Cienega, Midway Hospital, where we used to hospitalize our pediatric patients. Erwin Goldenberg and I used to talk about how we'd go in and find out what kind of treatment the nurses were giving. When we would ask, 'Did you give the shots of penicillin?' they'd answer, 'Oh, no. I wouldn't stick a little baby like that with a needle,' things like that."[18]

Physicians such as Ray Marcus who had come from private practice and already had staff privileges at various hospitals, continued to hospitalize their patients in those facilities. But sharing facilities with the fee-for-

Floor plan and interiors of Permanente Medical Center on La Cienega Blvd.

service community would prove just as problematic in Los Angeles as it had in San Pedro. "The Methodist Hospital staff was afraid of us and against us," said Kay. "We had to have our men on the staff, and they finally arranged it. But while they were doing it, we had to have other people doing our surgery. There was one of the men doing our surgery whose father had originated the Methodist Hospital. But the other doctors were making it so hot for him that he had to quit. He said to me, 'Ray, I had to quit. It was like a Ku Klux Klan meeting. It was just horrible.'"[19]

While the established medical community was not excited by the advent of prepaid health care in Los Angeles, people were. After the Retail Clerks joined, the culinary workers soon followed. "That was a big strain on us," said Ray Marcus. "We still had our original sixteen doctors and suddenly we got another 25,000 members, so now we're taking care of 50,000 people with the original Group plus a few more. The strain was enormous."[20]

Ray Kay turned his attention to recruiting physicians to take care of the growing membership, an effort that would involve and engage him throughout his professional life. "I felt that my most important job," said Kay, "was getting doctors and picking good doctors, and I think it was really the most important thing that I did for the Group. I really picked some wonderful doctors!"[21]

Throughout 1951 and 1952, Ray Kay continued to build the stable core of physicians he wanted prior to forming a partnership, and in Kay's thinking it had to be a partnership and not a corporation. When interviewed in 1985, Kay made it clear that only a partnership would enable SCPMG to operate as he and Sidney Garfield had envisioned. "Well, let's go way back to when Garfield and I were dreaming," said Kay. "We always felt the doctors had to have their own partnership — that they didn't want to work for anybody. They had to participate and have it as theirs. [. . .] Periodically people would say, 'Well, gosh, shouldn't we change to a corporation so that it would be better economically?' Well, if we were going to change to a corporation it meant that we had to divest ourselves of our employees. And that we never wanted to do. [. . .] Our employees in our organization meant too much to us, and we therefore went over it two or three times, and each time we decided we were going to stay as a partnership. [. . .] When Dr. Frank Murray became head [Dr. Murray would become SCPMG Medical Director in 1982] the other [Permanente Medical] groups became corporations. Then again there was a push as to whether we should incorporate. And again we decided we did not want to do it because we did not want to divest ourselves. I've tried not to butt in any more than I can help, but that was one decision I butted in on. I told Murray very strongly what I thought [. . .] and he agreed with me."[22]

SIGNING THE FIRST PARTNERSHIP AGREEMENT

By late 1952, Ray Kay believed that the Medical Group was finally ready to form its partnership and make the transition from employees of Sidney R. Garfield, MD and Associates into an organization of partners who did not "work for anyone." On January 1, 1953, thirteen physicians signed the Southern California Permanente Medical Group's first Partnership Agreement. In addition to DR. RAYMOND KAY, SCPMG's first Regional Medical Director, the senior partners included:

DR. LEONARD S. BUCK. Dr. Buck went on to develop the Ear, Nose and Throat Department at the Los Angeles Medical Center. In addition to serving as Chief of Service of ENT at the Sunset facility, Dr. Buck was instrumental in developing ENT departments in the other Medical Centers.

DR. RENE CAILLIET. Dr. Cailliet had been one of Ray Kay's residents at LA County Hospital and would go on to establish the Department of Physiatry (Physical Medicine) for SCPMG.

DR. ERWIN D. GOLDENBERG. Dr. Goldenberg was working as a pediatrician with the Medical Group in Fontana when Ray Kay invited him (along with Dr. Irv Klitsner) to become SCPMG's first co-Chief of Pediatrics. Together, Drs. Goldenberg and Klitsner developed the Pediatric Department at the Los Angeles Medical Center and guided the development of similar departments throughout the Region. In 1975, Dr. Goldenberg stepped down as Chief of Pediatrics at Sunset and returned to clinical practice in the Pediatric Department at Panorama City.

DR. JACK HALLATT. Dr. Hallatt had been recruited by Dr. Kay from the Permanente Hospital in Oakland to join the Medical Group as Chief of OB/GYN. He would later become co-Chief of OB/GYN (with Dr. T. Hart Baker) at the Los Angeles Medical Center.

DR. IRV N. KLITSNER. Dr. Klitsner had also been a resident at LA County Hospital under Dr. Kay, then began his career with Kaiser Permanente as a staff pediatrician in San Francisco. Later, Ray Kay recruited Dr. Klitsner to join Dr. Erwin Goldenberg in starting SCPMG's first Pediatric Department. Dr. Klitsner would go on to become Area Associate Medical Director in Panorama City and the Regional Associate Medical Director-at-Large of SCPMG. Dr. Klitsner then returned to clinical practice in Panorama City where, in the 1980s, he would develop SCPMG's adolescent health care program.

DR. CHARLES W. KNERLER. Dr. Knerler had also been recruited by Ray Kay from Oakland to become SCPMG's first Chief of Dermatology.

DR. EDWARD A. LOEB. Dr. Loeb was the Southern California Region's first pediatrician, having started with the Medical Group in Fontana in 1945. He would continue working as the Chief of Pediatrics in Fontana.

DR. ROY MIRANDA. Dr. Miranda, an OB/GYN, had been on the medical staff in Fontana since the early 1940s.

DR. ALVIN L. SANBORN. Dr. Sanborn would serve as Area Associate Medical Director in Fontana until June 1972, when he was appointed as Assistant to the Regional Medical Director, a position he held until he retired from SCPMG on December 31, 1975. Dr. Sanborn then returned to Fontana as a staff physician where he was instrumental in developing the Preventive Medicine Department and the Multi-Phasic Health Appraisal.

DR. FREDERICK H. SCHARLES. Dr. Scharles would serve as one of two Associate Directors (along with Dr. Herman Weiner) assigned to help Dr. Kay run the organization. Dr. Scharles, also a practicing internist, was specifically charged to represent SCPMG in its dealings with the Health Plan and Hospitals. He and Dr. Weiner were often described by Ray Kay as "my key guys."

DR. HERMAN WEINER. Dr. Weiner served alongside Dr. Scharles as an Associate Director. For his part, Dr. Weiner was made Head of Medicine and placed in charge of all outlying clinics. Dr. Weiner would succeed Dr. Kay as SCPMG Medical Director in 1970.

DR. JOHN H. WINKLEY. Dr. Winkley would become the Chief of Surgery at the Los Angeles Medical Center. In addition to being SCPMG's first general surgeon, Dr. Winkley also performed cardiac surgery, orthopedic surgery, neurosurgery, and GU surgery.

Although Sidney Garfield had been instrumental in getting the Medical Group to the point of partnership, he would not become an SCPMG partner. In 1952, Henry J. Kaiser had appointed him Medical Director of Kaiser Foundation Health Plan, Inc. and Kaiser Foundation Hospitals. Dr. Garfield would, however, continue his close association with SCPMG as it continued to grow and develop in the decades to come.

CHAPTER THREE

THE 1950S . . . GROWING PAINS

"The fifties were a struggle —
all the way through."

— *Irv Klitsner, MD, Board of
Directors, SCPMG*

LEFT
*Blueprint for the Panorama City
Medical Center*

INSET
*Garfield and Kaiser review plans for
three new hospitals to be built almost
simultaneously. Next to Kaiser is a
drawing of the proposed Los Angeles
Medical Center*

GROWING PAINS

THE 1950s would be tough years for the newly-formed Southern California Permanente Medical Group. Even before the first Partnership Agreement was signed, many conflicts and crises were already brewing. Within its first months and years, SCPMG would be thrust into battles with the Health Plan, the Kaisers, the unions, disgruntled physicians and the local medical societies that attacked the Group's very existence.

Yet, even while juggling one conflict after another, SCPMG never lost sight of its goal — to develop a viable medical program to care for the Health Plan's Southern California membership; a membership that would grow from 70,000 at the end of 1952 to 273,000 by the end of the decade.

MEDICAL SOCIETY OPPOSITION

The attack on SCPMG by the established fee-for-service community was not unexpected. The Group had already been confronted with opposition in Fontana and Harbor City, but now that it was entering Los Angeles, the medical societies turned up the heat. In their minds, the territory of "real doctors" was being invaded by a bunch of "communists" practicing "socialized medicine." The SCPMG physicians were nothing more than "captive doctors," beholden to the vast Kaiser empire; their patients, also "captives," forced to shun their own private-practice physicians for "some Health Plan doc who'd barely squeaked through medical school." SCPMG would spend much of its first decade wrapped in this hostile and unwelcoming environment.

"Anybody associated with the Permanente Medical Group," recalled Dr. Irv Klitsner, "was considered an outcast. I had good friends who I was with during my residency program who suddenly wouldn't speak to me anymore. I had relatives who wouldn't speak to me anymore. And, worse than that, we started getting bad publicity. The publicity was that we were staffed with doctors who couldn't make it any other way, we were socialized medicine, we were impersonal in our care, we were incompetent in our care. [. . .] And we were Kaiser doctors, we were employed by somebody who wasn't a physician."[1]

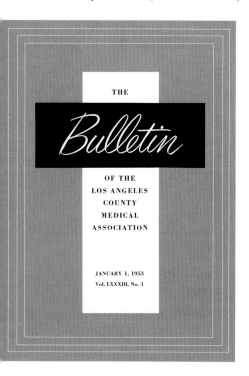

THE

Bulletin

OF THE
LOS ANGELES
COUNTY
MEDICAL
ASSOCIATION

JANUARY 1, 1953
Vol. LXXXIII, No. 1

While much of the ostracism was overt, some was more subtle. Dr. Sam Sapin, who would go on to become Chief of Pediatrics at the Kaiser Permanente Panorama City Medical Center as well as SCPMG Associate Medical Director of Clinical Services, described his own experience in the mid-1950s when he was practicing at the Los Angeles Medical Center (LAMC). "I decided that I would try to get on staff at Children's Hospital which was just across the street from LAMC," said Sapin. "I started attending at their pediatric cardiology clinic which met about once a week. After I'd been there for about a month or so, the physician in charge said, 'Why don't you try to get on staff here at Children's? By the way, doctor, where is your office?' I said, 'It's just across the street here. I work with Permanente.' His face fell and he didn't say anything. I went ahead and put my application in and got my recommendations. After about six months, I kept calling the office and saying, 'What's happening on the application?' They kind of hemmed and hawed. They never turned me down, but they never acted on my application either."[2] (Dr. Sapin then applied to UCLA where he was accepted.)

SCPMG physicians weren't the only ones being shunned. Their wives were blacklisted from social organizations, especially those related to the American Medical Association and the local county medical societies. Soon, the ostracism began to negatively affect the Group. "We were having a hard time keeping some doctors because of their wives and the way they were treated by fee-for-service doctors' wives," said Sidney Garfield. "We found out that a lot left not because they were unhappy with their work, but because their wives were unhappy, which made them unhappy."[3]

The opposition of established medicine was not only making it difficult to retain physicians, but also to recruit them. "At a time when we were recruiting staff physicians," recalled Irv Klitsner, "the county medical society decided we weren't good enough to belong to their society and if we couldn't belong to the county medical society in those days, we couldn't take our specialty boards. So can you imagine the problem we had recruiting somebody who'd spent a lot of years as a physician going through medical school, going through a residency, saying 'Hey, we've got a great program, a great way to practice medicine, of course, you won't be able to join the county medical society, and if you don't, you won't be able to take your boards because right now they don't see us as being a reputable organization.'"[4]

"To combat the specialty board issue," said Dr. Ray Marcus, "our lawyers and Dr. Kay wrote away to the boards and told them our specific problem. Most of the boards then passed a ruling that for the [Permanente] doctors out here, that they don't have to be members of the county medical society because they're being obstructed, so that's how far it went."[5]

One of SCPMG's chief attackers was Dr. Paul Foster, a well-established dermatologist and President of the Los Angeles County Medical Association during 1953. Prior to becoming President, Foster seemed to have few complaints about the Permanente Health Plan or the physicians in the Medical Group. In fact, Dr. Buck Wallin recalled that he'd referred patients to Dr. Foster from the La Cienega medical office, and Foster had no problem accepting the business. But when Foster ran for the presidency in late 1952, he jumped on the anti-Kaiser bandwagon. In issue after issue of The Bulletin of the Los Angeles County Medical Association, Foster railed against the "closed panel" Health Plan and warned fee-for-service physicians against allowing more Permanente expansion. Opposition to the Kaiser organization was the only plank in Foster's campaign platform. It would be enough. He won the election.

After assuming office, Dr. Foster's vicious attacks continued in his column titled, "Your President Says." In truth, Foster's hostility toward prepaid group practice was less about ethics and quality of care than economics. The rise of prepaid group practice frightened Foster and many others in "organized" medicine. The California Medical Association, the American Medical Association and Morris Fishbein, publisher of The Journal of the American Medical Association, never missed an opportunity to denigrate the Permanente program and position it as a threat to the status quo. For his part, Foster not only vilified the program, but also took every opportunity to link it to Henry Kaiser, as if that would prove his point that Permanente physicians were merely pawns of the great industrialist. In March 1953, Foster wrote in his column: "Mr. Kaiser has attempted to build a better mousetrap in many fields — shipping, automobiles, and general construction — and now he has turned his full-blown efforts in the direction of American medicine with a project he has chosen to call 'Permanente.'"[6]

The implication was clear; Kaiser might have the power to drive fee-for-service physicians out of business. Foster urged his fellow physicians to act before it was too late. In the same March 1953 column, Dr. Foster wrote: "The biggest problem we face right now is one of

HENRY J. KAISER ON THE AMA

The American Medical Association is frightened of anything that they think is a foot in the door which would affect their business. Naturally they'd be frightened, but they've been frightened of all these various plans, ours in particular. They've never been happy about ours; and they've never been happy about any plan, except those doctors who participated in it and who had the job of serving the people and feel human needs and had no concern with how it was paid for. I find that among our doctors they love the thing because they are able, without regard to expense, to take care of that patient the way [they] should be taken care of.

— *Henry J. Kaiser, interviewed for CBS news, September 27, 1960*

SIDNEY GARFIELD AND THE AMA

I'd like to ask the editor of the Journal of the A.M.A. just one question. Here are maybe a hundred thousand general practitioners in the country — how are they taught medicine? They're taught at modern medical schools that are the highest form of group teaching, of teamwork teaching that is. Who ever heard of a one-man medical school, of solo medical teaching of all the branches of medicine, in modern times? What modern medical teacher would have the gall, the brass, the presumption to teach all the medical disciplines? Then these medical students, these poor boys and girls, taught all these disciplines by the finest teams of doctor teachers in history, are supposed to go out and take care of 85 percent of all our illnesses — alone.

— *Paul De Kruif, quoting Sidney Garfield's response to an attack by the Journal of the American Medical Association in the mid-1940s, in his book* Life Among the Doctors, *p. 398.*

complacency — persuading physicians who are satisfied with the status quo that their way of living and practicing is not as safe as they might think. Living proof of this fact is evident in every corner of our Southern California harbor town of San Pedro, where one Association member has observed: 'The people in larger areas like Los Angeles can perhaps absorb an operation like Permanente without any noticeable pain. Down here, however, we're a small area with a limited number of available patients. Permanente peddles a product that fishermen and cannery workers like to hear, and we're finding that professional ability and niceness don't make up for the price bait they offer.'"[7]

Another warning from Foster in June 1953: "Your President has, on previous occasions in this publication, set forth the two challenges which he is convinced must receive prompt and definite offensive measures if California medicine is to survive as we now know it: Not necessarily in order of importance, these two challenges are Henry J. Kaiser's Permanente Health Plan and the blueprint for organized labor's health protection which has emerged from the so-called Weinerman Report."[8] Individual physicians were not immune from attack either, as Foster characterized many members of the Group as "those who failed to make a go of their own practice and have found it much simpler to pick up a monthly check from an employer."

Dr. Foster also communicated directly with Ray Kay, at one point sending him a letter demanding an investigation of SCPMG and other Kaiser entities: "It is assumed...that you are and will be prepared to make available...any and all documentary or other evidence having to do with ownership, control, purposes and services of the Permanente (or Kaiser) Foundation, the Permanente (or Kaiser) Health Plan, of the Permanente (or Kaiser) Hospitals, Inc., and their inter-relations, and the relation thereto of the partnership...of physicians functioning for and on behalf of any of the aforesaid organizations."[9]

SCPMG responded to Foster's call for an investigation by hiring lawyers acceptable to the LA County Medical Association, to look into the allegations. The lawyers verified that the Medical Group was indeed an independent partnership of physicians who did not "work for" Mr. Kaiser, putting to rest the "captive doctors" argument. To combat the idea that patients were also "captive," SCPMG established the policy that any consumer group joining the Health Plan must offer members at least one alternate plan to give them a choice about their medical care provider.

In spite of these efforts, the Medical Associations of both LA County and San Bernardino County continued to reject SCPMG physicians for membership. Many partners pushed Ray Kay to sue the medical associations, but SCPMG's lawyers urged a more conciliatory approach, which finally seemed possible, at least in Los Angeles, after Paul Foster left office at the end of his term in December 1953.

Dr. Foster's successors, Dr. J. Philip Sampson (President, 1954) and Dr. Ewing L. Turner, (President, 1955) did not, in Ray Kay's opinion, share Paul Foster's "pathological" fear of the Medical Group or the Health Plan, nor did they wish to continue Foster's battles. Ultimately, Drs. Kay and Turner agreed that there was

IMPORTANT DATES IN SCPMG'S HISTORY

1953
Los Angeles Medical Center opens

1954
Kaiser Permanente Medical Center moves from Kaiser Steel Mill to its current location on Sierra Avenue in Fontana

no justifiable reason to continue rejecting SCPMG physicians for medical society membership and that such rejections were in fact illegal. SCPMG agreed not to file suit for admittance, believing that such drastic action would permanently dash any hopes of reconciliation. For his part, Dr. Turner agreed to urge his members to accept the SCPMG physicians.

"Ironically," said Kay, "once we no longer had a problem obtaining medical association membership, few of our physicians took advantage of the privilege. On numerous occasions it was proposed that the Medical Group pay the physician's medical association dues, but though we encouraged their membership we did not feel the enormous expense of paying our physicians' dues was the best use of Health Plan members' dollars."[10]

INTERNAL CONFLICTS AND CRISES

At the same time that SCPMG was taking its hits from the outside and fighting for acceptance in the larger medical community, the Group faced severe internal conflicts. Somewhere at the core of almost every conflict was the issue of control; the idea that some "non-physician" entity would try to control the Medical Group and chip away at its autonomy. Ray Kay would have none of it. As he and Sidney Garfield had learned from Garfield's desert experience, the physicians must be in charge. It was a principle that Kay was willing to fight for and, especially in the 1950s, he would have to.

WORKING THINGS OUT WITH THE UNIONS

One of SCPMG's first conflicts was with some of the unions, based on the unions' belief that the plan was for their members and should offer what they wanted it to offer. Ray Kay had experienced the potential danger of union interference years earlier in Fontana, when the steelworkers' union had tried to force him to keep a sub-par optometrist on staff. Now, in LA, Kay started to get similar pressures, especially from Joe De Silva, head of the Retail Clerks Union. Kay had great respect for De Silva. He thought he was a "remarkable guy," imaginative and a great leader. But Kay believed that De Silva wanted to tell the Medical Group what to do and how to do it. Specifically, De Silva wanted SCPMG to offer a psychiatric program for his members. He also wanted the Medical Group to develop some kind of mechanism to resolve member complaints about coverage or medical care.

Around this same time, another union (Kay did not remember which one when interviewed in 1985) was pressuring SCPMG to hire more black doctors. Kay certainly had no problem from a racial standpoint, but he resented the union telling him who to hire and told them in no uncertain terms, "We cannot have any interference at all. If your union in any way wants to invade our right to pick the doctors [. . .] then I'd rather you pull your union out of the Health Plan."[11] The union backed down, but it was clear that the Medical Group would need to work things out with the unions in a way that satisfied both sides.

1956

SCPMG becomes the first medical group to sign the Medical Service Agreement, establishing a contractual partnership with the Kaiser Foundation Health Plan and Kaiser Foundation Hospitals.

1957

Harbor City Medical Center opens

1958

Panorama City Medical Center approved (opens in 1962)

Kay started by launching a series of meetings with members of the Retail Clerks Union in 1953–54 to educate them about the program. Kay and Joe De Silva would meet with two to three thousand union members at a time, telling them how to use the Health Plan and where to obtain services. Soon, meetings were held with other large consumer groups to introduce them to the staff, services and plans for their members' care.

The Medical Group also set up "grievance committees" to meet Joe De Silva's request for a way to resolve member issues and complaints. These committees, which would later evolve into the Membership Service Department, were initially for members of the Retail Clerks Union only, but soon proved so effective that similar committees were established for other large groups, including the Longshoremen in the harbor area.

Each grievance committee included representatives from the Medical Group, the union, and the Health Plan. Members typically came to the committee with complaints about their doctors or about care they'd received in a hospital. Sometimes, members would seek care outside the plan, then expect the plan to pay for it. The grievance committee attempted to resolve such issues, including paying for outside service when appropriate.

Although Ray Kay would come to regard the Membership Service Department as one of the Group's smartest moves, he was concerned that it often placed a third party between the patient and his or her physician. Therefore, patients and physicians were encouraged to get back together and resolve problems on their own whenever possible, without interference.

And about Joe De Silva's request for psychiatric care for his members? That would be addressed as well, although it would take a few years to get the program off the ground. In 1961, SCPMG launched a psychiatric program at the Los Angeles Medical Center as a pilot project for the Retail Clerks. Dr. Philip Wagner, hired as chief of the new Psychiatric Department, assembled a group of full- and part-time psychiatrists, psychologists and psychiatric social workers to see patients from the Retail Clerks Union.

Initially, psychiatric services were provided only to patients referred by SCPMG physicians. At first, coverage was for outpatient care only, with 20 visits offered per year without charge. Additional visits cost $5 each. In November 1961, the Retail Clerks added a 30-day hospital program which was later expanded to 45 days. A year later, outpatient services were offered to patients who referred themselves. Soon, the program was expanded beyond the Retail Clerks Union and opened to other Health Plan groups.

In 1966, the Retail Clerks decided to set up their own mental health department, so Dr. Wagner and part of the staff moved to union headquarters. Dr. Edward Green, who had been Assistant Chief since January 1965, then became Chief of Service.

By offering psychiatric services to the Retail Clerks, the Medical Group demonstrated its commitment to provide members (both union and non-union) with the services they wanted. The psychiatric program would also prove the wisdom of starting new programs as pilot projects, to help work out the kinks on a small scale and determine demand. Many other programs would be started in the same manner over the years, including an alcohol abuse program which was initially launched in LA for federal employees. The small program soon became large, so that each area eventually had its own Addictive Disease Department (as it was then called), with services available to all members.

FONTANA THREATENS AUTONOMY

Ray Kay would often describe a situation that arose in Fontana as one of SCPMG's greatest crises. It began in 1955 when a group of Fontana physicians presented Kay and Alvin Sanborn, their Medical Director, with a White Paper listing their complaints. While there were many individual points raised, they all boiled down to a couple of key issues: the physicians who had signed the White Paper claimed that Ray Kay and the Los Angeles office had too much control, and they had too little. Furthermore, they questioned Sanborn's leadership and communication skills. Dr. Larry Crowley, one of the physicians who had signed the White Paper, went so far as to travel to Oakland and present his colleagues' complaints directly to Eugene Trefethen, Henry Kaiser's right-hand man.[12] The Fontana group demanded that they be given more autonomy and that Ray Kay remove Alvin Sanborn from his job. Both Kay and Sanborn were taken off guard by the White Paper and stunned by its allegations. "I was never so hurt," Kay recalled.[13]

Although the Fontana physicians were not proposing complete separation from SCPMG, they did want to become an autonomous small group within the organization. Dr. Kay was adamantly opposed to the concept of autonomy for Fontana and to the idea of replacing Alvin Sanborn, in whom he had great faith and confidence.

While Ray Kay was determined that Fontana would not "break away" from SCPMG, he was willing to strengthen local administration by improving representation and communication. His first step was to appoint Larry Crowley as Assistant Medical Director at Fontana. Although Ray Kay had been hurt by Crowley's actions in signing the White Paper (and perhaps chagrined by his visit to the Kaiser organization), Kay considered him an outstanding surgeon and leader and hoped that he would help improve communication and restore a degree of confidence and morale.

For awhile, it seemed to be working. In July 1956, Dr. Crowley reported that "the problems in Fontana have been settled or are in the process of being settled and that the morale is much improved."[14]

But by early 1957, the winds of discontent were once again blowing in Fontana, as the complaints about

autonomy and Dr. Sanborn's leadership refused to die. Now the Board of Directors was urging Kay to remove Sanborn and replace him with Dr. Crowley. Kay refused, saying, "I wouldn't do it because I felt it would have been really unfair to remove a guy [Sanborn] who really was doing a fine job, and put somebody else in."[15]

Sanborn would remain as Medical Director in Fontana, but the autonomy issue would continue to be a point of contention. The conflict came to a head on September 30, 1957 in a meeting between the SCPMG Board of Directors and representatives from Fontana. The key topic of conversation — should SCPMG be divided into smaller groups or continue as one group with one franchise?

Then finally, a decision. SCPMG would not decentralize. "It was finally accepted," said Ray Kay, "that there was strength and stability in the one-group structure; that complete autonomy of areas within the Group would lead to chaos. [. . .] Thus we decided that we would remain as one group with one governing board and one administrative team — all functioning together with common motivation and objectives."[16]

By 1959, even though the conflict seemed to be resolved, some physicians, including Dr. Larry Crowley, remained unhappy with the situation and decided to leave the Medical Group to enter private practice. Soon afterwards, Ray Kay announced his own decision: he would remain SCPMG Medical Director in Los Angeles, but would also return to Fontana and resume his previous role as co-director with Alvin Sanborn. They divided duties, with Dr. Sanborn in charge of the day-to-day administration, while Dr. Kay supervised the Chiefs of Service and other management personnel. Kay let it be known that this arrangement would work, telling the Chiefs of Service, "By God if you don't support what we're doing, and you don't support Dr. Sanborn, well, you're out."[17] After a year or so, things were working so well in Fontana that Kay basically pulled out of his direct involvement. Alvin Sanborn would remain as Medical Director in Fontana until he was appointed as Assistant to the Regional Medical Director in 1972, a position he held until his retirement in 1975.

COMING TO TERMS WITH THE KAISER ORGANIZATION

Although SCPMG was part of the Kaiser organization, the Group firmly believed it should have some say in its own operation and destiny. That belief would be put to the test in the 1950s when Henry Kaiser developed an all-consuming interest in the program and began to exert unprecedented control.

Kaiser had left the medical care program pretty much alone until 1951. As long as his workers were receiving good health care, he was happy. But what sparked Henry Kaiser's interest in medicine was his marriage in June 1951 to a young nurse, Alyce Chester, who had cared for Kaiser's first wife, Bess, during her final illness. Henry, then 68, and Alyce, 34, married less than four weeks after Bess's death. It would be an understatement to say that the marriage caused a firestorm of controversy among Kaiser's family and business associates, still in deep mourning for the woman they'd affectionately called "Mother Kaiser." Kaiser's sons, Henry Jr. and Edgar, opposed the marriage, shocked by what they saw as its inappropriate timing. Kaiser however, who'd been happily married to Bess for 44 years, explained that he dreaded living alone and could not work without a companion.

But regardless of what anyone thought (or gossiped) about the marriage, Alyce was an extremely capable woman; selected by Sidney Garfield not only as his personal assistant but also as the nurse to care for Henry Kaiser's beloved wife. Alyce, whom everyone called "Ale" (pronounced Allie), was not content just to lead the life of an executive's wife and was looking for something to do in the medical field. She hoped her new husband would join her. Kaiser was more than willing. He soon announced that he was going to build a new Permanente hospital for Ale in Walnut Creek, about 20 miles east of Oakland and just a short drive from the Kaiser home.

The news came as a total surprise. In all the discussions about planned growth there had never been any mention of a hospital in Walnut Creek. But now, Kaiser had unilaterally decided to build one. What's

HENRY J. KAISER

A

C

F

B

A. *Nationally known and admired, Kaiser's speeches were often broadcast over network radio*

B. *President Roosevelt (right) visits the Richmond Shipyards escorted by Henry Kaiser and his son Edgar (second and third from left)*

C. *Bess and Henry Kaiser at the dedication of the Permanente Hospital in Oakland, August 21, 1942*

D. *Alyce and Henry Kaiser on their wedding day in June 1951*

E. *Henry Kaiser (top center) with a group of workers from the Richmond Shipyards*

F. *Henry Kaiser visits with some young patients at the Kaiser Rehabilitation Center*

G. *Henry Kaiser at the blackboard at the Kaiser School of Nursing. He is explaining his favorite poems by Tennyson*

E

G

more, Walnut Creek would not be just any hospital, it would be a "luxury" facility that would also be available to fee-for-service physicians. In fact, the fee-for-service providers were crucial to the operation because there were not enough Health Plan members in the Walnut Creek area to support a Permanente hospital. Sidney Garfield (who would soon marry Ale's sister, Helen) agreed with the plans for Walnut Creek, believing that the medical care program would benefit from Kaiser's increased involvement.

The Permanente physicians in Northern and Southern California felt they had been broadsided by the announcement. Not only had they had no voice in the decision, they were also in the midst of building hospitals in their own areas, one in San Francisco and one in Los Angeles, and needed money for those efforts. Buck Wallin, still without a medical center in Harbor City, also felt left out in the cold. "We started to feel rejected down there, almost as though we didn't exist. We had criteria for building hospitals, and membership

WALNUT CREEK HOSPITAL

TOP LEFT
The circular design of the first Kaiser-Permanente-built medical offices in Walnut Creek was considered "futuristic"

TOP RIGHT
"Push Button Hospital" was Look Magazine's description in 1953 when the hospital was hailed as the nation's most modern. Numbers highlight the innovations conceived by Dr. Garfield

RIGHT
Ingenious drawer system between nursery and maternity rooms permitted mothers and babies to experience a new innovation called "rooming in"

was one of them. They had 5,000 members. We had 26,000," he said with a laugh.[18]

Yet, here was Kaiser, using funds that the Medical Groups helped generate to build his own hospital for fee-for-service physicians! Calling Walnut Creek Kaiser's "own" hospital was not an exaggeration. The Medical Groups had not been consulted about its construction or its cost, whereas the cost of hospitals in San Francisco and Los Angeles was being closely monitored.[19] The Groups were also ignored about staffing the new facility,

dubbed by many as the "Country Club." Ale Kaiser personally selected Walnut Creek's medical staff, often hiring or promoting newcomers over other physicians who had been with the organization since the Coulee Dam days. The quality of the physicians Ale Kaiser selected was never an issue; even those physicians she had bypassed agreed that she had selected outstanding medical talent for Walnut Creek. It was the manner of their selection that rankled. Just as painful was the rumor that the Walnut Creek physicians were earning higher salaries than their colleagues in other areas, another tough pill for the Permanente physicians to swallow.

Also alarming to many physicians was the proposal in the early 1950s that the medical program entities adopt the name Kaiser and drop "Permanente." This idea had actually come up in 1945 when the program went public. Sidney Garfield himself proposed the name change, believing that the word "Permanente" had little meaning outside the organization and that the Kaiser name was easier to pronounce and known throughout the country. But executives of the Kaiser companies voted against the change in 1945, in part because of opposition from the established medical community. Many Kaiser executives and their wives were friends with fee-for-service physicians and their wives and didn't want to jeopardize those relationships by linking the Kaiser name to a controversial medical program. Kaiser executives were also against the change because they believed the medical program would fail after the shipyards closed at war's end. They did not want the valuable Kaiser name, associated with so many successful companies, tied to a losing proposition. "Ironically, of all the industries these executives were running, only the Health Plan would survive and thrive in anything resembling its original form," wrote Dr. John "Jack" Smillie, a physician and administrator with The Permanente Medical Group (TPMG) in Northern California from 1949 to 1981 and author of the group's definitive history.[20]

But when the name-change issue rose again a few years later, the Kaiser executives no longer opposed it. Nor did the Northern and Southern California Medical Groups object to adopting the Kaiser name for the

Health Plan and Hospitals, but they were adamantly opposed to being labeled as Kaiser Medical Groups.

"There had already been the insinuation by organized medicine that we worked for Mr. Kaiser," said Ray Kay, "and we did not in any way want to give credence to this concept."[21]

Sidney Garfield asked Ray Kay to be the one to tell Henry Kaiser that the Medical Groups would not be using his name. Dr. Kay accepted the role of group spokesman and broke the news. In reply, Henry Kaiser said, "Of course, of course, I wouldn't let him [Kay] use my name. I don't want them to use my name. I wouldn't let them use my name." It was, as Kay recalled, "just as if we'd taken candy away from him."[22]

Henry Kaiser reluctantly agreed that the Medical Groups should retain the "Permanente" name, while the Health Plan and Hospitals would now become "Kaiser." The name change became official on January 9, 1953. The organization itself would now be known as Kaiser-Permanente; the hyphen representing the linkage between the entities. [The hyphen was dropped in 1985.] While the refusal to take on the Kaiser name was based on the Medical Groups' desire to assert their autonomy, it also underscored their resentment of the Walnut Creek hospital and Henry and Ale Kaiser's intrusion into territory the physicians regarded as their own.

There'd be further intrusion as well when, about this same time, Henry Kaiser began to advocate the breakup of the Medical Groups into separate partnerships, exactly what Fontana would propose a few years later. The Medical Groups saw this as a "divide and conquer" tactic on Kaiser's part, his way to control obstreperous doctors. But the partners believed that only a large, united group could stand up to Kaiser, something they were starting to see as an absolute necessity. Henry Kaiser went so far as to have articles of incorporation drawn up for a separate Walnut Creek medical group that he and Ale could control. But the Permanente physicians at Walnut Creek, including Dr. Wallace Cook, who'd been personally selected as Physician-in-Charge by Ale Kaiser, refused to leave the partnership. When confronted with the Walnut Creek opposition to

his plan, Kaiser made no secret of his irritation, but eventually backed down. The Medical Groups would remain whole. Many believe that it was Walnut Creek's refusal to become a separate entity that saved the Permanente Medical Groups, at least as the large, united organizations we now know.

Although SCPMG had been far less involved in the Walnut Creek controversy than their Northern California counterparts, the Medical Group was certainly concerned, not only by Kaiser's interference but also by his attempts to cut the physicians out of the decision-making loop. Their fears were only reinforced when Kaiser announced, in effect, that doctors should take care of patients and leave the "business" of health care to knowledgeable businessmen.

Kay interpreted Kaiser's remark as a desire to isolate the Medical Groups, with no representation or influence in the Foundation, the Health Plan or the Hospitals. "This effectively reduced them to the status of managed employees," noted John Smillie, who added that "Kay was also concerned about the security of the Permanente physicians."[23] Kay's concern grew out of his belief that a day might come when the Health Plan would actually terminate its relationship with the Medical Groups and start contracting with other physician groups.

It seemed obvious that the relationship between the Medical Groups and the other Kaiser health care entities was breaking down and mired in distrust. Throughout 1954, Drs. Ray Kay, Fred Scharles and Herman Weiner, as well as representatives from The Permanente Medical Group, met with Kaiser representatives in an attempt to work things out. At one meeting, on June 7, 1955, Henry Kaiser surprised the physicians by offering to sell them the medical program in its entirety — the Hospitals, the Health Plan — everything. He and his organization would step aside. About this same time, Kaiser made a similar offer to Ray Kay in a meeting the two men had at the Hotel Bel-Air in Los Angeles. "We talked until about three in the morning," Kay remembered. "Finally at the end of this time he [Kaiser] said, 'You know, Raymond, if you and your Group want to buy the hospital and the health plan we'll sell it to you.' And I said, 'Oh, Mr. Kaiser, we couldn't do that.' I knew he was bluffing. I knew he wasn't going to sell it to us. But I thought it was worth exploring."[24] The Permanente physicians did briefly explore the idea of buying the program but concluded that the expense was prohibitive. Besides, they wanted to save the medical care program as it existed, if only they could work out a way to become involved in the policy and operation of the Hospitals and Health Plan.[25]

But by July 1955, when nothing had been resolved, Henry Kaiser called for a summit conference at his Lake Tahoe estate to determine if it was possible, or even desirable, for the entities to continue working together. It was common for Kaiser to hold tough bargaining sessions at his home where he felt in control; and the upcoming meeting had every indication that it would be as difficult as they come.

The battles leading up to the Tahoe Conference in 1955 had brought the organization to a state of paralysis. As Cecil Cutting later explained, "Expansion was stopped, membership was stopped, spending of money was stopped; everything ground to a halt." It was, in Dr. John Smillie's words, the program's "nadir year." The physicians at Tahoe knew they'd either come back with some sort of agreement or the organization was going to implode.[26]

At first glance, the Tahoe Conference seemed a battle of poorly matched contenders. Here were physicians, trained in medicine, not business, going head-to-head with some of America's most skillful businessmen and a team of lawyers, all of whom were there to protect Kaiser's interests. But Ray Kay, as SCPMG's representative, and his Northern California counterparts, were adamant in defending Medical Group autonomy, even if it meant dissolving the program they had worked so hard to build.

Kay, who had fought with Henry Kaiser before and would again, more than held his ground against the great and powerful man. Periodically, when the discussions became heated, Henry Kaiser would tell Kay, "You're challenging me, Ray Kay. You're challenging me, and I won't stand for it." Kaiser would then start to storm out of the room. His son, Edgar, would calm him down and the negotiations would continue. "He did that

THE LITTLE BLACK BAG

So what was in that little black bag? For house calls, physicians carried a BP cuff; Class 3 and 4 narcotics (injectable and pills); tongue depressors; ophthalmoscope; otoscope; digitalis (IV and tablets); penicillin and sulfa drugs; #21 and 18 scalpels; and a surgery pack. Many bags were stolen for drugs, even when kept in the trunk of a car.

— *As told to Steve Gilford by Buck Wallin, MD, SCPMG Retired*

about three times," Kay recalled. "But we got by that meeting, and when we finally ended up that meeting and we had come to a point of agreement, he [Kaiser] came and put his arm around me and said, 'I knew we could work it out, Ray Kay. I knew we could work it out.'"[27]

They did work it out. After three days of meetings, on July 19, 1955, the assembled group came to several points of agreement, among them: that the medical care program must be preserved and that all entities must dedicate their efforts to working together; that an Advisory Council, composed of key members of the Health Plan, Hospitals and Medical Groups would be permanently established; that major problem areas were to be covered by contract; that the Health Plan would not develop competitive groups in the regions; that the Hospitals and the Medical Groups would be supported in their basic needs and that any excess revenue would be equally distributed between the two groups.

The heart of the Tahoe Agreement: that all entities and their expertise were essential and that a working relationship based on partnership rather than control or domination must be developed.

Following the Tahoe Agreement, the Advisory Council met at least once a month for the next six to seven months to discuss issues and grievances. Based on these discussions, Eugene Trefethen came up with a proposal that would form the basis for a contract between the Kaiser Foundation Health Plan and the Permanente Medical Groups, known as the Medical Service Agreement. In the late spring of 1956, Trefethen presented the proposal to SCPMG. Trefethen had decided to work with the SCPMG physicians first, before going to The Permanente Medical Group in Northern California, largely because of Ray Kay. Kay was the undisputed leader of SCPMG with the support to speak for the group, whereas TPMG leadership was divided and not as clear cut.

LEFT TOP
The boathouse at Fleur du Lac, Henry Kaiser's Lake Tahoe estate

LEFT TO RIGHT
Henry J. Kaiser, Sidney Garfield, MD, Raymond Kay, MD,
Cecil Cutting, MD, Fred Scharles, MD, Eugene Trefethen,
Wallace Neighbor, MD, Herman Weiner, MD

TPMG was also against adopting the Medical Service Agreement, preferring to continue operating as they were. Ray Kay was amenable to change. "Despite the confrontational style of Ray Kay," wrote John Smillie, "relations between the physicians, the Health Plan, and the Hospitals in Southern California were actually functioning more cordially than in the north. [. . .] Southern California was also in a period of major growth and was hence doubly anxious to achieve arrangements that would allow it to get on with the business of providing prepaid comprehensive health care to the rapidly expanding Southland."[28]

In mid-1956, SCPMG began working under the Medical Service Agreement on a trial basis. The agreement proved so successful that within six months the Health Plan and SCPMG accepted it, without reservation. SCPMG would become the first Permanente Medical Group to sign the Medical Service Agreement, which went into effect on January 1, 1957. The Permanente Medical Group in Northern California finally signed the agreement in 1958.[29] This Medical Service Agreement, signed in the mid-1950s, has been the basis for all the Permanente Medical Service Agreements signed since then.

The Medical Service Agreement essentially restructured the organization by establishing that The Kaiser Foundation should no longer function as an ownership or holding entity and that, from now on, there should be three major entities in the program: the Health Plan, the Hospitals and the Medical Groups. The Agreement identified key areas of authority and responsibility for each of the entities and, most important, stated that responsibility and control had to be shared, that no entity should make unilateral decisions, especially on issues related to the entire program such as Health Plan membership growth.

The Agreement established that each Region have a high degree of autonomy in conducting its operations and that each Region should be financially autonomous in terms of revenue and accountability. It established that the Health Plan would pay the Medical Groups a set amount per month for each Health Plan member, with the exact amount to be adjusted periodically to reflect increases in the cost of living as well as increases in the cost of providing medical services. The Agreement also included an incentive compensation system in which excess Health Plan revenues would be equally divided between the Medical Groups and the Hospitals.

One of the most important parts of the Medical Service Agreement was the Franchise Clause which gave each Medical Group a franchise, or the exclusive right, to care for all Health Plan members in a specific Region. Making the Franchise Clause a contractual issue eased the Medical Groups' fear that the Health Plan would contract with competing medical groups in an area, robbing the Permanente groups of the patient base they had worked to build. The Franchise Clause also bound the Permanente Medical Groups to provide services only for Health Plan members.

The signing of the Medical Service Agreement was one of the most important milestones in SCPMG's history. For the first time, it established a contract between a Permanente Medical Group and the other Kaiser entities which encouraged cooperation and a spirit of partnership. Although the Medical Service Agreement did not result in total harmony, it was a solid start.

STRUGGLING WITH MEMBERSHIP GROWTH

Ever since the Permanente Health Plan opened to the public in Southern California, first in Fontana, then in the harbor and metropolitan Los Angeles areas, membership had been on the rise. And while SCPMG welcomed growth, it was also concerned about its ability to build facilities and recruit enough physicians to sustain quality care. And what was enough? Ray Kay had developed a ratio: two beds per thousand people and one doctor for every thousand members.[30]

But the burgeoning membership was straining the ratio and threatening to upset the desired balance between membership, facilities and staffing. To prevent an imbalance, the Medical Group pushed the Health Plan to control enrollment. The Health Plan pushed right back. "They wanted to get as many members as they could," said Kay. "[. . .] That was their job."[31] The

Health Plan tried to help by closing membership to new groups and individuals much of the time, but it was not a solution that made anyone very happy. As soon as possible, the Health Plan would reopen, igniting new battles with the Medical Group.

The Medical Group and the Health Plan tried to achieve a proper balance between membership, staff and facilities, but it would not be easy. As Dr. Kay would write in his 1979 book, Historical Review of the Southern California Permanente Medical Group, "The growth of the Health Plan membership and the efforts to support this growth with adequate staff and facilities has been the story of our organization ever since."[32] Over the years, SCPMG would launch many efforts to help control growth, including forming the Planned Enrollment Program Committee in 1966 to develop principles for a "controlled, planned enrollment." But for the 1950s, SCPMG would attempt to meet the membership challenge by stepping up efforts to build both staff and facilities.

RECRUITING THE "RIGHT KIND OF DOCTORS"

The desire to balance Health Plan membership with staff caused SCPMG to dedicate considerable time and effort to recruiting during the 1950s. Over time, a kind of mythology has developed about Ray Kay's unique recruiting style. Many, including Sidney Garfield, would often claim that when Dr. Kay lived in Fontana he'd bring potential candidates into his home and keep them there for about a week to "make sure they were the right kind of doctors." Kay admits that many physicians stayed with him and his wife in Fontana, but simply because they didn't have anyplace else to live. The invitation to stay, he would say, was not for recruitment purposes.[33]

The myth undoubtedly survives because it does have the ring of truth. Ray Kay's commitment to hire "the right kind of doctors" was widely known and unwavering. As Sidney Garfield would say, "He wasn't going to make any mistakes on getting men who didn't have their heart in that type of medicine."[34]

THE LIGHTER SIDE OF HOUSE CALLS

In the early 1950s, SCPMG physicians made house calls, traveling to and from members' homes in their new Kaiser-Frazer automobiles. Each house call was five dollars (or less!) per visit. For the members, a real bargain. For the physicians, oftentimes, a lifelong memory.

"I recall one house call where I saw a mother and four children. After examining all five of them for the five-dollar fee, the mother asked me, 'Doctor, can you tell me why the dog is vomiting?' I went right back to Ray Kay and told him, 'We've got to start charging more for house calls.'"

— Al Miller, MD, SCPMG retired

"One rainy night a woman called and asked if someone could please come out and look at her sick child. I suggested that she bring the child to the clinic where he would have access to equipment and a lab if they were needed. The woman on the phone sounded surprised, 'Are you kidding, I wouldn't send a dog out on a night like this!'"

— Erwin Goldenberg, MD, SCPMG retired

"A parent called in late one night with a question about an asthma patient, her son. She sounded quite concerned. I asked her how the patient was doing, about his breathing and his color. She interrupted me saying, 'He's asleep now, doctor. We're new here and I heard that you were available 24 hours a day. I just wanted to check and make sure it was true.'"

— Irv Klitsner, MD, SCPMG Retired

SCPMG recruited both locally and nationally. The Group held dinner meetings throughout Southern California to tell interns and residents about the program. SCPMG physicians with staff appointments at area hospitals were encouraged to keep them and establish personal relationships with young residents and interns with the hopes that they might join the Group.

SCPMG placed ads throughout the country and kept in touch with potential candidates. At least once each year, the Group sent its own "outstanding physicians" around the country to conduct interviews. "Usually in February or March we would take off for recruiting medical doctors," said Buck Wallin. "We'd done our own research as to what Air Force bases were demobilizing, how many men were going to be transferred out of [the military] or whatever. We would milk the military, particularly, and also the graduating classes of large city hospitals."[35] Irv Klitsner was another member of the recruiting team. "Ray Kay gave each of us territory, like traveling salesmen, and we went back to the schools. I went to the Midwest, Wisconsin and Chicago, and the areas around there. We made contact with the medical schools. We arranged for meetings with the resident staff, and we arranged for personal interviews with people who were finishing their training. We went to the Army bases, and as a bonus Ray let me go to New Orleans because I was a jazz enthusiast and a saxophone player. I loved to go down there. I would go to Tulane, spend a couple days there and recruit people while we would go and listen to Pete Fountain."[36]

Sometimes, Ray Kay went on the recruiting trips too. Irv Klitsner recalled one particularly memorable occasion: "On a recruiting trip to Chicago, he [Kay] got caught in a snowstorm. He had sent his suit, the only suit he had with him, to the cleaners. We had an appointment for interviews that night, and Ray's suit didn't come back, so he put on his overcoat over his underwear and interviewed doctors with me."[37]

When Kay was urged to use experienced non-physician recruiters, he declined. "We felt strongly that since we were primarily a partnership of doctors," he said, "that was the image we wanted to project. [. . .]

We were very anxious to avoid any association that might give the impression that we were 'big business' rather than a professional group."[38]

Many potential candidates were invited out to Southern California for an interview. "As an inducement for them to come visit," recalled Irv Klitsner, "we used to pay their way out and their expenses while they were here. We paid only half of what their expenses were, but if they joined the Group we would reimburse them the other half. So, it was not completely a vacation for these guys. They had to take some risks in coming out."[39]

Kay or one of his key associates spent considerable time with each interested physician. "Ray Kay would never hire people on the spot," noted Klitsner, "and neither would we when we went out on these recruiting trips. If I saw somebody who was a surgeon or a dermatologist, or an OB/GYN, or a pediatrician, I'd let him know where the potential openings were. If I felt that he was really interested, we would invite them out to meet with the chief of that service who would have the final say to hire them or not."[40]

Conversation during the interviews usually focused more on the benefits of group practice than salary. "We talked more about that than we did salary," said Kay. "And I think it worked to our benefit because the key guys we got came to us, not because of salary, but because they believed in it. I think that's what carried us through the rough years that we've had — those dedicated guys. It took people with vision to really join us then against the medical societies, and with our relatively small salary. They had to really believe in us. And those are the guys that have made this what it is today!"[41]

Compensation offered in the early 1950s had been established in the Articles of Partnership. In the first Articles of Partnership in 1953, a salary ceiling of $18,000 per year had been set for the partners (administrators were paid a bit more). In 1954, the ceiling for partners was raised to $23,000; and in 1957, raised again to $26,600.[42] Initially, Ray Kay had wanted all physicians in the Medical Group to receive the same pay. However, by the late 1950s, he realized that the "all for one, one for all" idea was unrealistic. SCPMG would have to pay higher salaries to attract and retain well-trained physicians and those in specialties in which there were shortages (at the time, these included ENT, Neurosurgery, and Orthopedics). The bottom line: some physicians in the Group would be paid more than others. "It was necessary to compete in the market, yet we made every effort to prevent undue differences in compensation between the various specialties," said Kay.[43]

One of the more interesting benefits provided to all SCPMG partners, starting in 1953, was the use of Kaiser-Frazer automobiles, a product of Henry Kaiser's car company. Sidney Garfield had arranged the perk in part, some believed, to help the struggling auto manufacturer stay afloat. Many partners resented having to drive the Kaiser autos, described as beautiful but "grossly underpowered." The issue would become moot in 1955 when Kaiser closed the auto plant and the partners were able to choose other makes of cars. In

1963, the Group decided to get out of the car business entirely and replaced the auto allowance with a salary increase of $150 a month.[44]

While SCPMG would work to boost salaries and benefits to competitive levels, Kay believed that SCPMG's "major emphasis was not to 'maximize physicians income' in dollars but to make our professional way of life worthwhile."[45] What SCPMG was offering physicians then, as now, was the opportunity to practice in a stimulating professional atmosphere, comparable to the environment they had found in medical school. The Group enabled each physician to function autonomously, yet be able to freely consult with peers at any time. The Group freed the physician of the "business" of being a doctor and allowed him to establish doctor-patient relationships without having to negotiate payment. It offered the chance to have the kind of "planned life" often impossible in private practice.

Henry and Ale Kaiser standing beside their Kaiser Darrin Car in front of the El Mirador Hotel in Palm Springs

STRUGGLING TO KEEP PACE WITH FACILITIES

Sidney Garfield believed in a concept often called "Garfield's theory of creative shortages." The idea behind the concept was simple — if facilities didn't quite match demand, then doctors and Health Plan would come up with creative ways to use the resources they had.[46] Garfield didn't necessarily drag his feet on building new facilities, but he wanted to make sure they were truly needed before proceeding. There was little question in the 1950s that Southern California needed facilities; yet, in keeping with Garfield's theory, facilities would always be slightly behind the curve in meeting demand.

During the 1950s, the Kaiser organization would build, or start to build, four major medical centers:

Los Angeles (opening in 1953), a new hospital in Fontana to replace the steel mill hospital (opening in 1954), Harbor City (opening in 1957), and Panorama City (approved in 1958 and opened in 1962).

Initially, Sidney Garfield had hoped that these medical centers would integrate both hospitals and medical offices in order to save on equipment and travel time for physicians visiting their hospitalized patients. That was how it was done in Northern California, where the medical offices were considered the beginnings of a medical center. But the concept wouldn't work in Southern California — the area was just too large. It would be impossible for any one facility to be convenient to all members, even with LA's sprawling

freeway system. So the pattern developed in Southern California that each specified service area would have a large medical center (which would include a hospital and some medical offices) and a number of satellite medical offices in the surrounding area. These neighborhood medical offices would each have its own team of one or more general practitioners (functioning as the day-to-day family doctors), pediatricians and internists. Patients needing specialty care or hospitalization were referred to the Group's nearest medical center.

BUILDING THE LOS ANGELES MEDICAL CENTER

In 1951, the Permanente Foundation purchased what was then a section of Barnsdall Park at the corner of Sunset Boulevard and Edgemont Street for $200,000 to build the Los Angeles Medical Center. The plan was to build a 200-bed hospital. "We didn't want to build any hospital bigger than two hundred beds," recalled Ray Kay. "We thought it got too impersonal and too big."[47]

The seven-story hospital opened in February 1953 with 224 beds, with what the Los Angeles Times described as a "wealth of innovations," all of which had been implemented by Sidney Garfield. In his role as Medical Director of Kaiser Foundation Health Plan and Kaiser Foundation Hospitals, Dr. Garfield (who'd once dreamed of becoming an architect) would help design

many Southern California facilities, including the Los Angeles Medical Center. Garfield had always been very interested in hospital design, especially with those elements that contributed to better patient care. Back in the Contractors General Hospital days, he'd installed newly-invented venetian blinds to keep out the glaring desert sun. He not only installed air conditioning at Contractors General, but also insisted that the entire hospital be air conditioned, probably making it the first hospital in California to be so equipped. He personally selected a soothing color scheme and placed flowers and radios in the wards, believing that environment played an important role in the healing process.

For the LA Medical Center, he came up with the idea of multiple nursing stations (one for every four rooms, or eight patients) instead of a single station for all nurses on a floor. The idea was to reduce the time the nurses spent traveling to and from rooms and increase the time they could spend with patients (Garfield had actually done time-motion studies on the topic!). The hospital featured central work corridors for medical staff and

FAR LEFT
Garfield and Kaiser examine plans for three new hospitals to handle the growing Health Plan membership. On the left is Los Angeles, on the right is San Francisco, and the model is of the proposed Walnut Creek hospital

LEFT AND ABOVE
Los Angeles Medical Center in the 1950s

separate outside corridors for visitors, based on Garfield's theory that the medical staff could work more efficiently if not impaired by visitor traffic. These separate corridors would be a feature of all Kaiser Permanente hospitals for the next couple decades. There were many self-service devices too, including electric beds with push-button controls and a built-in cabinet with water taps and radio and phonograph outlets.

But what really captured the public's fancy was the bassinet in each maternity room which a new mother could pull out from the wall like a drawer whenever she wanted to feed and care for her baby. Like most of Sidney Garfield's innovations, the "baby in a drawer" concept combined patient comfort and convenience with efficiency — a nurse did not have to take babies back and forth to the nursery. The "baby in a drawer" idea had been developed at Yale University and became a standard feature of the Kaiser Foundation Hospitals built during this time. The Los Angeles Medical Center was one of the first in the Kaiser system to use it. This early version of "rooming in" grew out of the belief that it was important that mother and newborn have time together as soon as possible — and the more time, the better.[48] This would be one of many innovations introduced by SCPMG over the years to enhance patient care.

The Sunset location soon proved too small to handle the ever-growing Health Plan membership and would eventually be forced to expand, first to 300 beds, then to 400, and finally to its current size of more than 600 beds.

BUILDING A NEW HOSPITAL IN FONTANA

By the early 1950s, the Fontana physicians were still working out of the original hospital built next to the steel mill. The Group decided to build a new facility in the town of Fontana, away from the steel mill site. They chose a site on Sierra Avenue, at the time a location surrounded by absolutely nothing.

Fontana would be built in stages, starting with the construction of two wards at the new location, one medical ward and one OB ward. The wards were run as

part of the steel mill hospital, giving Fontana two hospitals which were operated as one. The dual system soon proved cost prohibitive, so the Group decided to build a new hospital around the two new wards in town. The estimated cost of the new facility came in at around twenty thousand dollars per bed. Then Sidney Garfield devised a plan that would cost about one thousand dollars per bed. He proposed splitting the mill hospital into nine sections and moving them to the Sierra Avenue location. And that's exactly what was done. In 1954, the nine sections of the old mill hospital were transported, piece-by-piece through the streets of Fontana, six miles to the new location where they were reassembled next to the wards and connected by a new corridor.

ABOVE
Fontana Medical Center in the 1950s

RIGHT
Architectural drawing of Panorama City Medical Center

Irving Klitsner, MD, Geri Kurz and Ron Wyatt making an inspection as construction nears completion

BUILDING THE HARBOR CITY HOSPITAL

Harbor City had gotten off to a bumpy start in terms of facilities. Medical Group physicians had literally been evicted from the first offices they had rented in 1950. They were barely tolerated at the community hospitals where they sent their patients. When the Group finally found space to practice, it turned out to be over a dress shop in San Pedro. Later, the Group had offices in a converted motel on Normandie Avenue. Patients needing hospitalization were sent to the Kaiser Permanente medical centers in LA or Fontana. "Except for a bona fide emergency," said Dr. Buck Wallin, Area Associate Medical Director in Harbor City. "Then I'd authorize payment for the Sisters of Mercy at St. Mary's Hospital [in Long Beach.] [. . .] It was about a 15- to 20-mile trip, so we used to have some nice ambulance bills."[49]

But finally, in 1956 construction began on the new Kaiser Permanente Harbor City Medical Center off Pacific Coast Highway and Vermont Avenue. The 56-bed hospital opened in 1957 to serve the Harbor–South Bay membership of just over 46,000 people. Harbor City featured many of the same Sidney Garfield innovations used in other medical centers of the time, including separate corridors for staff and visitors, decentralized nurses' stations and a private nursery to keep mothers and babies together.

In 1982, a $25 million, four-story addition to the hospital would be completed. The 122-bed addition would increase Harbor City's total inpatient capacity to 277. The new addition housed a six-room operating suite, a 15-bed recovery room, a 20-bed intensive and coronary care unit, administrative offices, medical library, medical records and central processing.

BUILDING THE PANORAMA CITY "BINOCULARS"

In 1954, Ray Kay asked Irv Klitsner, then working as a pediatrician at the Los Angeles Medical Center, to supervise construction of a small primary care facility on Hamlin Street in North Hollywood to help care for the

San Fernando Valley's growing membership. The office opened in November 1954. Any doubt that this facility was needed was erased when the doctors driving to work on opening day passed a line of people three blocks long waiting for services.

Initially, the North Hollywood medical office was staffed by four Permanente physicians who hospitalized their patients at the LA Medical Center on Sunset Boulevard. Within a year, Dr. Klitsner would double the staff, but even that was not enough to take care of the Valley's population which was soaring at a rate of 12,000 people each month. By mid-1957 it became apparent that the San Fernando Valley members would soon need their own hospital.

In 1958, the directors of the Kaiser Foundation Hospitals approved plans to construct a hospital at Woodman Avenue and Cantara Street in Panorama City, close to the Valley's geographic center. Construction would begin in October 1960. Ray Kay and Irv Klitsner, as the designated Area Associate Medical Director of the developing area, selected a group to help plan and staff the new facility to be designed by Sidney Garfield.

Garfield decided to take a particularly daring approach in Panorama City. Instead of building a conventional square or rectangular structure, he chose a circular configuration, which resembled two side-by-side drums, or a pair of binoculars. Garfield selected the circular structure because it allowed him to place the nurses' stations in the center of the circles where they would be as close as possible to patient rooms, as opposed to traditional hospitals where nursing stations were often located at the end of a long corridor. Garfield had also reduced the distance between nurses and patients at the LA Medical Center by placing the nurses' stations along the corridors. Now, in Panorama City, they would be in the center of the circles. The idea, of course, was that the nurses would save considerable travel time and effort if their patients were close by. The patients would benefit too, secure in the knowledge that a nurse was only a few steps away. Garfield called his concept "circles of service." Sam Sapin, one of the group asked to work with Sidney Garfield on the new hospital, liked the design, calling it ideal for pediatrics. "You had the nursing station in the center and all the

rooms radiated from this center," he said. "With pediatrics, the nurses could actually see into every room. The patients, who were children, were not stuck off at the end of some rectangular floor."[50]

In his design of other more traditionally-shaped Kaiser Permanente hospitals, Garfield would also centralize nursing stations as much as possible by placing them in the middle of the floors. Although innovative in its design, Panorama City would be the first and last Kaiser Permanente hospital built with the circular floor plan, undoubtedly because of the many difficulties in construction and the necessity to secure more than 15 building code variances to build it.[51]

While the hospital was still under construction, Drs. Kay and Klitsner began reviewing the entire staff for prospective Panorama City Chiefs of Service. "We try to develop leaders from within our Group," said Kay, "selecting them two to three years in advance. This gives them time to choose their key staff men and establish solid professional foundations for their departments before the facility opens."[52]

When the Panorama City Medical Center opened in September 1962, it was hoped that the new facility would take the load off the Los Angeles Medical Center, and it did to a certain extent, although soon more facilities would be needed...a job for the 1960s.

BUILDING THE MEDICAL CARE PROGRAM

During the 1950s, as SCPMG coped with the challenges of forming a new organization, the Group also focused its efforts on improving the medical care program both for members and the physicians who cared for them.

IMPROVING HEALTH PLAN COVERAGE

In 1952, SCPMG initiated a visiting nurse program, under the direction of Vera Lund, to provide care for patients who no longer needed hospitalization but were unable to visit the clinic. In 1964, Dr. Herman Weiner, an Associate Medical Director, would establish a Home Care Program, which made both physicians and nurses available for home care visits. The program was started in Los Angeles, then expanded to all areas.

Dr. Larry Crowley, who would later co-author the Fontana White Paper, launched SCPMG's first Cancer Program in 1953 when he established a Tumor Registry in the Fontana hospital. Crowley went on to set up the Consultative Tumor Board in Los Angeles in 1954 and the Tumor Registry in 1955. The cancer diagnostic and treatment program of the hospital and medical staff, including the registry and board, was given its first three-year approval by the American College of Surgeons Cancer Committee in 1957. Similar programs with registries and boards would eventually be established in all the hospitals.

In 1954, the Group established a single vision optical finishing laboratory. Two years later, the lab began grinding its own glasses, which resulted in a significant savings. As Ray Kay noted in his book, as a result of these savings, patients' fees for glasses remained the same for the next eight years.[53]

Up until 1958, under the membership agreement, people who had a health problem before joining Kaiser Permanente (a "pre-existing" condition) were not covered for treatment of that problem. For instance, people who'd had a cardiac problem before becoming a Health Plan member would not be covered for cardiac care. This changed in 1958, when the pre-existing clause was discontinued for people who joined the Health Plan as members of a group (the pre-existing clause would still apply to members who joined as individuals). What this meant, of course, was that people would be treated for health problems they'd had before joining Kaiser Permanente. Ray Kay, on behalf of the Medical Group, welcomed the change, noting that it was now "possible for us to care for many deserving members who had formerly been deprived of care."[54] Kay noted that changing the pre-existing clause was especially advantageous for cardiac patients who had been ineligible for surgery because of pre-existing conditions, but could now receive care.

PHYSICIAN EDUCATION

From the beginning, SCPMG placed a strong emphasis on providing a continuing medical education program for physicians, based on Ray Kay's belief that "if you're going to get good doctors you've got to have a good educational program. If you're going to keep good doctors and keep them good, you're going to have to have an educational program."[55]

At first, physicians were given two half-days a week for educational activities such as medical meetings, organized rounds at various hospitals, teaching and research. In 1957, the partnership voted to make one of these half-days available for personal use and labeled it as unscheduled time. However, physicians were encouraged to combine this unscheduled time with educational half days to maintain their commitments as attending physicians and teachers at the various county hospitals and medical schools. The Chief of Service was authorized to allow three half-days, if necessary, for physicians to meet such commitments.

Providing physicians with even one half-day off was costly. "That's an expensive thing when you figure eighteen hundred doctors," said Ray Kay in 1985. "That's nine hundred doctor days. And when you figure three hundred dollars a doctor, say, or two hundred dollars a doctor, that's a big slug of money for the education. But we felt it was so important that we have always protected it and insisted upon it."[56]

SCPMG began holding annual medical specialty symposia in the 1950s, similar to those that Ray Kay had held during his days at the Los Angeles County Hospital. Initially, the two-day symposia were held for the medical, surgical, OB/GYN and pediatric departments, during which professors from around the country were invited to lead discussions and review papers presented by the staff.

In 1955, SCPMG's first residency program was started in the Department of Obstetrics-Gynecology by Dr. T. Hart Baker, who would become SCPMG's Medical Director in 1971. Dr. J. Fenimore Cooper began the residency in Urology in 1960, followed four years later by a Pathology residency, established by Dr. Jack Gordon. "During this period these physicians developed the basic principles for our residency programs," said Ray Kay. "They felt such programs should improve the quality of care by attracting outstanding physicians and stimulating them with the opportunity to teach house staff. They also believed that residencies should not be a source of 'cheap labor,' but would hopefully provide a source for future well-trained additions to the staff."[57]

A PROMISE OF THINGS TO COME

By the close of the 1950s, SCPMG had worked through some difficult issues. The Group had overcome major opposition from local medical societies and the fee-for-service community; it had developed programs to satisfy and serve its many union members; it had resolved a push for autonomy in Fontana and maintained the integrity of the group structure; it had signed a contract with the Kaiser organization that promised operation in a spirit of partnership; and it had built staff and facilities to care for the growing Health Plan membership.

The 1960s would see a new set of challenges, many sparked by the passage of the Federal Employees Health Benefits Act of 1960 and other legislation that would stimulate huge enrollment increases; so huge, in fact, that the Health Plan would be forced to close the program to new members for much of the decade. For SCPMG, the challenge would be to care for an increasing number of people with the same high standards set in the 1950s.

Contractors General Hospital

YOUR PRESIDENT SAYS THE TIME HAS COME

Editorial written by Paul D. Foster, MD, President of the Los Angeles County Medical Association (1953). Originally published in The Bulletin of the Los Angeles County Medical Association, *May 21, 1953, page 501. Reprinted by permission of the Los Angeles County Medical Association.*

To talk of many things;
Of corporations and captive patients
And free choice of physicians;
Of interlocking directorates
And tax-free, non-profit organizations;
Of industrial magnates — and controlled medicine;
And why the sea is boiling hot
And whether closed panels have wings.
(With apologies to Lewis Carroll)

In the Capitalistic, free-enterprise system of twentieth-century America, corporations have become an integral and important part of our thriving economy. Most of them do a good, profitable job for their stockholders and all, with few exceptions, are valuable arteries into the mainstream of our nation's economic life.

The term "corporation" in general, then, has no particularly evil connotations so long as it exists within the framework of strict economics and does not monopolize and devour the field in which it operates by masquerading as a "charitable, non-profit institution," and competing with small, individual businessmen who pay taxes and who do their share to support the community in which they live.

As we have said before on these pages; in the medical profession — as in many other phases of life — one predominant thing makes man akin to divinity; the freedom and the responsibility to plan our own lives, the right to earn, to hold, to enjoy, to dispose of our professional knowledge as we see fit.

The doctor who fails to live by that philosophy and who has so little confidence in his own ability that he succumbs to the lure of corporate medicine has, in effect, become a captive doctor. He has surrendered all the scientific and humanitarian values acquired in medical school by conforming with a closed-panel plan that makes a sick person a liability to both the plan and to himself. His incentive is no longer the self-satisfaction that comes with swift cure; rather it is to withhold treatment and to use cheapened short-cuts so that the plan can grow richer, bigger, and more powerful. The doctor working for someone else in this capacity cannot have undivided loyalty. His first allegiance is to the person for whom he works — and his second, and minor, loyalty is to the patient under his care.

And just as the doctor in tightly controlled closed panel systems is an automaton who dispenses treatment via directives from some higher source, so are some patients in closed panel systems captive. They cannot dismiss the plan physician and choose another outside the plan without sacrificing dues already paid. They cannot be sure they will ever see the same doctor twice during a course of treatment, for the simple reason that the disillusioned staff physicians themselves parade in and out of the plan so fast that there can be no continuity or established relationship between the captive doctor and the captive patient.

Permanente is growing bigger every day. In view of the fact that only 40 per cent of Kaiser patients use the health plan facilities, it is obvious that it would be entirely possible for them to some day treat half the state for nothing — so long as the other half pays the bills.

As a "California Medicine" editorial recently stated: "Our medically-trained minds cannot follow Kaiser's intricate inter-corporate entanglements, rental arrangements, partnerships, inter-organization contracts, and pooled personnel and purchasing arrangements. But we know that what Mr. Kaiser says will happen in Permanente, usually happens."

The accuracy of this observation was made clear to the author in a recent luncheon with Mr. Kaiser, wherein it was made plain that his medical venture is as much under his (a layman's) control as are his automobile and construction enterprises. He could not, in fact, embark on his expensive experiment without the subsidy he obtains from his other multi-million dollar enterprises. An example of this interlocking system is the fact that at least one of the men hired by the Kaiser Industries was, in fact, a king-pin in the medical plan — even though the plan was not required to pay his salary.

The parent organization controls the money out of which the health plan and its hospitals can borrow. Since the hands that hold the purse-strings also hold the power to supervise medical procedures, this means that doctors, hospitals, amount and kind of drugs, laboratory procedures, the number and kind of personnel, and the entire extent of services are directed by a layman's mind and hands. As long as the Kaiser contracts provide only for "the necessary medical care" and "the necessary surgical care," they have no fear of being broken down by over-usage [sic]. The shanghaied union member can only be treated in terms of that broad term "necessary."

Although Mr. Kaiser has stated to your President that the free choice of physician is an "outmoded concept," he is still making overtures to become part and parcel of recognized, ethical medicine. A considerable portion of this "Bulletin" is devoted to a factual study of those efforts.

As President of the Los Angeles County Medical Association, I urge every association member to read the documents carefully. When you have done so, I am certain you will agree with the resolution passed by the council at its last meeting, to be found on page 510.

Your President's mind is open to suggestions and ideas that will better the existing patterns of organized medicine. Try as he may, however, he cannot reconcile his medical training and ethical concepts with a dictatorial, closed-panel plan that is diametrically opposed to the ideals that have allowed Medicine to progress and grow strong as a guardian of health and as a guardian of freedom for both the doctor and the patient.

CHAPTER FOUR

THE 1960S . . . THE GOLDEN YEARS

"The fifties were really the key decade as far as our developing the foundation. Then we got into the sixties, which were the golden years. Everybody loved us."

— *Irv Klitsner, MD*

SCPMG Board Meeting
STANDING, L-R
Buck Wallin, MD, Eugene Strull, MD,
Fred Scharles, MD
SEATED, L-R
Ray Kay, MD, Al Sanborn, MD

UNLIKE the 1950s when the Southern California Permanente Medical Group had been rocked by one crisis after another, the 1960s would be an era of enormous growth, unmarred by serious conflict. In Southern California, the Health Plan found itself in the enviable position of facing virtually no competition. Consumer groups were literally waiting in line to sign up, sparked by the program's growing reputation for providing good care at a fair price. "We had more members than we could take care of," recalled Sam Sapin.[1]

Health Plan membership in Southern California would almost triple during the 1960s, climbing from just over 320,000 at the beginning of the decade to almost 900,000 by the end. For SCPMG, the key challenge at the beginning of the decade would be to support this growth with physician staffing, new facilities in new service areas and innovative programs to improve patient care in an organization that seemed to grow larger day by day.

UNPRECEDENTED ENROLLMENT INCREASES

While the Health Plan had grown at a steady pace during the 1950s, passage of the Federal Employees Health Benefits Act in 1960 caused enrollment to soar. For the first time, federal employees were given the option of selecting a prepaid group practice plan such as

Kaiser Permanente for their health care coverage. Thousands of people took advantage of the opportunity. State and local governments soon passed similar legislation, creating potential enrollment groups throughout Southern California. The impact on the Region was dramatic, driving membership up by 10–12% per year and forcing the Health Plan to periodically close off new enrollments. Often, SCPMG itself initiated the program closures out of concern that too many members would overwhelm the Group's ability to provide quality medical care.

Besides government employees, other employee groups were also pushing for membership, many at a time when the Health Plan was limiting or closing enrollment. In 1967, one such group was Lockheed Aircraft Company, then located in Burbank and one of the largest aircraft manufacturers in the world. Irv Klitsner estimated that Lockheed had about 15,000 to 20,000 employees who wanted to join the Health Plan, along with their families.[2] But at the time, said Ray Kay, "we were so tight on members that we couldn't take them." It was a tough situation and neither the Medical Group nor the Health Plan liked it. Recalled Kay: "So the Health Plan felt terrible and they said, 'This could be a big group of members.' And I said, 'I can't help it. We just can't take that many,' and I said, 'Let's try this. Let's say we'll take two thousand this year, and two thousand more the next year, and do it gradually.' The Health Plan said, 'Oh, they'll never do that. They'll never stand for it.' I said, 'Hell, let's try it.' It worked fine, and we got Lockheed that way."[3]

This kind of enrollment ingenuity was necessary during the 1960s to manage Health Plan growth. In addition to the Lockheed plan which admitted several thousand members at a time, other methods used to control growth included temporarily closing membership to new groups and individuals. Sometimes, open enrollment periods in existing groups were discouraged. When SCPMG expanded service to San Diego in 1966, new contracts between employee groups and the Health Plan gave the Health Plan the specific right to limit enrollment.

While keeping up with growth usually meant hiring more physicians and building more facilities, the Medical Group would also introduce some innovative programs to, in Ray Kay's words, "free physicians for more demanding activities." One of the most successful and enduring of these was the nurse practitioner program.

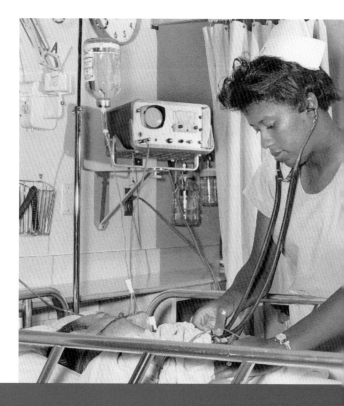

1962

Panorama City Medical Center opens

1964

Nurse practitioner program launched in Panorama City

THE NURSE PRACTITIONER PROGRAM

During the 1960s, with membership on the rise, SCPMG needed so many new physicians that Drs. T. Hart Baker and Fred Scharles spent as much as three months each year traveling around the country searching for qualified physicians in all specialties. But recruiting alone could not keep pace with demand. "Our needs were so great," said Ray Kay, "that we realized our physicians must have assistance in caring for their patients."[4]

At the time, there were few, if any, programs to train or provide the kind of "physician assistants" Kay was talking about. However, a successful pediatric nurse practitioner training program had been developed in Denver, Colorado. When he learned of the program, Sam Sapin, then Chief of Pediatrics in Panorama City, embraced the concept and started to explore the idea of using nurse practitioners in his department. The program seemed promising on several counts — first, it had the potential to ease the physician staffing problem. And second, Sapin thought it also might solve another critical problem that was developing in the pediatric field throughout the country — that of physician boredom. "Pediatricians seemed to be getting tired of the routine," Sapin recalled, "talking to the parents about whether you start cereal first or applesauce first. It didn't seem to be challenging."[5] Sapin believed the "boredom factor" was causing some physicians to shy away from pediatrics or to leave the field and he did not want the same thing to happen in Panorama City.

The potential benefits of using nurse practitioners seemed too great to ignore. So in 1964, the Pediatric Department in Panorama City started a nurse practitioner program simply enough, by hiring one nurse to perform well-baby care. Dr. Jack Lipshin agreed to train and supervise the nurse and be the all-around mentor for the program. Later, several more nurses were hired for well-baby care and were also trained within the department. The nurses worked in tandem with the baby's pediatrician at each visit. "What we did," said Sapin, "if the visit was fifteen minutes, we'd assign the nurse ten minutes to discuss feeding and other matters, and then the pediatrician did the physical exam for five minutes. So we were saving physician time while increasing the amount of information and discussion with the patient. As far as I know, it was the first program of its kind in the Kaiser Permanente system and one of only a few in the country."[6]

Like many new programs, some physicians liked it and some didn't. The physicians who were against the program were usually those who liked well-baby care. They thought that if they turned this "fun part" of their practice over to the nurse practitioners they'd be left to care only for sick children. Other physicians welcomed the idea that nurse practitioners would take over the "less interesting" part of pediatrics, leaving them to handle the more challenging cases. "We had some bloody battles," said Sapin. Believing the battles might prove too divisive, Sapin recalled telling Irv Klitsner, then Area Associate Medical Director at Panorama City and a pediatrician himself, "Irv, I've had it. I'm giving this thing up." "No," replied Klitsner, "Stick to it. We've got to do it."[7]

1965

Bellflower Medical Center
opens

1966

SCPMG expands service area
to San Diego

1968

Construction begins on West
Los Angeles Medical Center

The program continued and became increasingly popular with both physicians and patients. About a year after the nurse practitioners began working with patients, the department gave parents a questionnaire, asking their opinion of the program. "They loved the program," said Sapin. "The parents felt they could talk more readily to these women nurses than they could to the men pediatricians and talk about the diaper problems and the feeding problems. They felt that they had more of a compassionate listening ear. The satisfaction with the well-baby program was just great. So we said, 'We're on the right track.'"[8] The Panorama City program started with the nurse practitioners caring for well babies only. This soon proved so successful that the program was expanded under the direction of Dr. John Fuerth to train nurse practitioners to care for well children and adolescents, and later on, for sick children and adolescents.

As begun in Panorama City, the nurse practitioner program proved that specially-trained nurses could successfully perform certain medical services, freeing physicians for the tasks that truly demanded their skills. The program also proved that it could have a significant favorable impact on the ratio of physicians to patients. With these kinds of results, it seemed only logical to build up the nurse practitioner program and expand it to other departments.

That would be done in 1971 under SCPMG's newly-created Department of Medical Manpower, headed by Ray Kay following his retirement as SCPMG Medical Director in 1970. Kay had been favorably impressed by the nurse practitioner program in Panorama City. He'd seen evidence that it was helpful in terms of staffing and had the potential to control costs while maintaining quality.

One of Kay's first steps was to get other specialties, beyond pediatrics, involved in using nurse practitioners. "What Ray did was use a fantastic approach," recalled Irv Klitsner. "He got all the Chiefs of Service together and asked them, 'What are you doing that somebody with lesser training could do as well or better than you're doing now?' And, 'How could that help us in patient care?' He got a laundry list from practically

every service except dermatology. They said, 'Nobody can do anything that we can do.'" But even the dermatologists finally agreed that non-physicians could perform certain functions and do a good job of it. Before long, according to Klitsner, "they had wart nurses, acne nurses, things like that."[9]

While many medical groups and physicians around the country hired nurse practitioners who had been trained elsewhere, Ray Kay wanted to set up his own training program. In 1971, Kay launched the Southern California Region's first formal program to train nurse practitioners in Pediatrics, Internal Medicine and OB/GYN. "It's a one-year program," said Kay, "and we pay their salaries while they are taking that year of training. They spend two days a week at lectures, and three days working with patients, with the doctors teaching them as they work with the patients. At the end of that year they're damn good."[10]

In 1975, the Region's nurse practitioner program became affiliated with the California State University Los Angeles School of Nursing. In later years, as numerous nurse practitioner training programs started being offered throughout California, Kaiser Permanente decided that it would no longer co-sponsor such programs, but would hire their graduates.

Over time, many departments would use nurse practitioners as part of the medical care team. In the early 1980s, Dr. Kenneth Bell, then Chief of Obstetrics at the Anaheim Medical Center, decided to make certified nurse midwives part of the obstetrics team. Ten years after their introduction, nurse midwives were delivering about 60 percent of the babies at Anaheim.[11] Later in the 1980s, Dr. Les Zendle, then Regional Physician Coordinator for Elder Care, and nurse practitioner Patricia McDonough set up a program for nurse practitioners and physician assistants to help Health Plan members living in nursing homes. To evaluate the program, Dr. Zendle received a grant from the Sidney Garfield Memorial Fund. The fund had been established in Dr. Garfield's honor in 1987 to encourage just this sort of innovation and exploration into new models of care that would benefit the entire community. Dr. Zendle's study showed that the elderly patients seen

by the nurse practitioners were extremely happy with
the personalized care. In addition, because of the nurse
practitioners, the nursing homes sent fewer patients to
emergency rooms for the evaluation of minor problems.

SCPMG's decision to use and train nurse
practitioners was definitely paying off. Noted Kenneth
Bell, "As an organization, we were committed to
extending the availability of care in the most cost-
effective ways, and with the highest quality. What we
found was that the nurse practitioner did all those
things. They actually improved care."[12]

"He'd talk to you until you'd agree."

— *Irv Klitsner about Ray Kay*

SCPMG Board Meeting
STANDING, L-R
Buck Wallin, MD, Eugene Strull, MD, Fred Scharles, MD, Sam Sapin, MD
SEATED, L-R
Ray Kay, MD, Al Sanborn, MD, Irv Klitsner, MD, Nathan Omlid, MD

INSET LEFT
*Aerial view of the Bellflower Medical
Center, 1966*

INSET RIGHT
Bellflower physician, staff and patient

BACKGROUND
*Site of the Bellflower Medical Center
The city was formerly known as Dairyland*

AREA EXPANSION

By 1960, SCPMG physicians were caring for patients at a growing number of satellite medical offices and at three major medical centers, in Fontana, Harbor City and Los Angeles. But three

medical centers simply weren't enough, and the problem was more than just membership numbers. It was also geography. In the sprawling Los Angeles basin, many members (and potential members) wanted a medical center closer to their homes.

To meet the demand, the Southern California Region would open two medical centers in the 1960s, in Panorama City (1962) and Bellflower (1965). The Group would expand service to San Diego in 1966 and launch plans to build a new medical center in West Los Angeles which would open in 1974.

PANORAMA CITY MEDICAL CENTER OPENS

The Panorama City Medical Center had been approved in 1958 to meet the growing demand for services in the San Fernando Valley. Construction began in October 1960, and by September 1962 the unique binocular-shaped structure was ready for use.

Before Panorama City opened, Valley residents had been hospitalized at the Los Angeles Medical Center. Everyone hoped that Panorama City would relieve some of the pressure on Los Angeles. It would help, "but it still wasn't enough," said Ray Kay, "so we were soon working towards developing a facility in Bellflower."[13]

EXPANDING SERVICE TO BELLFLOWER

While the Bellflower Medical Center was much needed, the facility itself would turn out to be something of a nightmare. The problem began when Sidney Garfield asked the Medical Group to use the same design for Bellflower that had been used for the Santa Clara Medical Center in Northern California. Garfield liked the plan which housed both medical offices and hospital in the same building. He also liked the fact that using the same design for both facilities would save time and money, especially in architects' fees.

It sounded like a great idea, but the Medical Group did not like the design Garfield was proposing. "We felt that there was not a good balance between clinic space and hospital beds," said Ray Kay, "that clinics and hospital in the same building would make modifications and expansion very difficult; that clinics, and especially waiting rooms, were grossly inadequate; and that the flow between a hospital and clinic in the same building was going to cause crowding and confusion."[14] [In the mid-1980s, the Area Associate Medical Directors decided to change the designation from "clinics" to "medical offices." Of course, when Dr. Kay was writing in 1979, the word "clinic" was the accepted term and widely used.]

Even though Garfield's plan seemed flawed, SCPMG approved it. In July 1965, the Bellflower Medical Center opened at the corner of Rosecrans and Clark Avenues with 192 beds and offices for 60 physicians. Buck Wallin, who had been serving as Area Associate Medical Director in Harbor City, moved over to take the reins at Bellflower. Dr. Wallin was replaced in Harbor City by Dr. Harry Shragg who had been working as a surgeon at the medical center.

The combination of hospital beds and medical offices at Bellflower soon proved to be as unworkable as Ray Kay had predicted. "The result was a center that never functioned well," said Kay. "It was a constant source of discontent, and eventually had to be rectified by extensive and expensive modifications and additions."[15] In 1976, 108 beds would be added to the Bellflower

Medical Center, as well as support services and facilities for 62 physicians, at a cost of $17 million.

Although Panorama City and Bellflower were supposed to lighten the burden on the Los Angeles Medical Center, neither did, at least not enough to make much difference. What's more, Panorama City and Bellflower were having problems serving their own growing populations, much less trying to absorb additional patients from LA. "Our most pressing problem," recalled Ray Kay, "was still relief for Los Angeles."[16]

BRANCHING OUT TO WEST LOS ANGELES

Virtually the moment the Bellflower Medical Center opened its doors, plans were in the works to build yet another medical center, this one to be close enough to Sunset to give real help. Planners checked out a number of sites, to the east, southeast and west. Finally, they picked a location in West Los Angeles on Cadillac Avenue just off the Santa Monica Freeway.

In 1965, Harry Shragg, then Area Associate Medical Director in Harbor City, was asked to form a staff and

TOP
San Diego Clinic in the 1960s

RIGHT
West Los Angeles Medical Center

plan facilities for the new center in West LA. Dr. Shragg asked doctors, nurses and staff who were already working in existing Kaiser Permanente hospitals to help with the new design. He was especially interested in what they thought about current projects in Panorama City and Bellflower. What did they like? What worked? What didn't?

Shragg's team voted to retain the very successful central nursing units of Panorama City's circular towers, but avoid the expense of circular construction. They also wanted to avoid the pitfalls of Bellflower with its combined hospital and medical office floors.

The solution was to build a rectangular facility with adjacent, but separate, medical office and hospital structures, each with its own elevators. "We hoped this separation would allow us to expand without interfering with existing operations and to avoid the confusing traffic flow that existed in most of our centers," said Ray Kay. "Both goals were accomplished."[17]

Planning and building the West LA Medical Center would take nearly seven years (from 1968 to 1974), but as Ray Kay said upon its completion, the new facility was "beautiful and functionally well conceived." However, Kay would also note that finances had caused one floor of the Medical Center to be eliminated. "As a result," he said, "the center was already too small the day it opened."[18]

In 1970, while waiting for the new West Los Angeles Medical Center to open, the Medical Group had converted a convalescent care building on Manchester Avenue in Inglewood to a Medical Center with hospital and medical office facilities. After West LA opened in 1974, the Inglewood facility continued as a skilled nursing center.

REACHING OUT TO SAN DIEGO

Strangely enough, it was not SCPMG who first proposed setting up San Diego, it was The Permanente Medical Group from Northern California. Just as strange, TPMG's San Diego venture was to have no connection to the Kaiser Hospital or Health Plan entities! It would be under the total ownership, control and operation of The Permanente Medical Group. TPMG would provide all the physicians for the operation and run its own health plan and hospital. Meanwhile, in Northern California, TPMG fully intended to remain part of the Kaiser organization and continue its relationship with the Kaiser Foundation Health Plan and Hospitals.

TPMG felt they had good reason for wanting to establish a separate operation. For years, the Group believed that the Boards of Directors of the Health Plan and Hospitals were making unilateral decisions that should have been made jointly. But while the relationship may have improved somewhat by 1961, TPMG's leadership was still, in the words of John Smillie, "uncomfortable about sharing 'their' program with the Health Plan."[19] According to Dr. Morris Collen, an original TPMG partner and member of the Executive Committee, "The Medical Group felt that it was the primary agent in the health care program, and that Hospital and Health Plan were of secondary importance."[20] To prove its point, TPMG decided to set up its own program in San Diego "to show the Kaiser organization that MDs could run their own enterprise."[21]

There was, however, a slight problem. The San Diego area actually "belonged" to the Southern California Permanente Medical Group, not TPMG. Years earlier, the two medical groups had agreed to divide California at the Tehachapi Mountains, located south of

Those visiting the Kaiser Permanente Hospital in Hawaii today will not see the luxury facility that Henry Kaiser built in 1958. That famous structure met a dramatic end, befitting its dramatic beginning. In 1986, the Honolulu Medical Center building was dynamited to rubble in a planned implosion. The dramatic event was featured in an episode of the Magnum PI television series starring Tom Selleck. As part of the plot, the Selleck character was trapped in one of the building's elevators just as disaster loomed. Would Magnum die as the building came crashing down around him? Would our hero escape in time? Of course.[43]

TOP
Kaiser reviewing plans for the Honolulu Medical Center

MIDDLE LEFT
Kaiser supervising construction

MIDDLE RIGHT
Publicity shot with the Honolulu Medical Center in background

BOTTOM
Advertisement for the Kaiser-owned Hawaiian Village Hotel

Bakersfield. The agreement gave TPMG the right to expand above what was called "The Tehachapi Line" and SCPMG below it. Since San Diego fell within SCPMG's territory, the project needed to be cleared with Ray Kay.[22] "As we had no plan to expand to San Diego at that time we had no immediate objection," recalled Kay. But that didn't mean Kay thought TPMG's San Diego venture was a good idea. As he later noted, "we did feel that establishing a separate and competing health care program in this region was unwise and a breach of intentions mutually agreed upon with the Kaiser Health Plan."[23]

In spite of these reservations, SCPMG gave the Northern California group permission to proceed. But Ray Kay was absolutely insistent that TPMG not use the names Permanente or Kaiser in connection with their new program. To avoid conflict, The Permanente Medical Group chose the name Pan-Medical, Inc. for their program in San Diego.

In July 1961, TPMG purchased the 46-bed Lake Murray Hospital near San Diego as the starting point for Pan-Medical. Morris Collen, then Physician-in-Charge of the medical center in San Francisco, took a leave of absence to move south and run the operation. He began setting up the hospital and looking for a home for his family. Everything seemed to be going according to plan, at least until Henry Kaiser heard about it.

Kaiser was now living in Hawaii and when he heard what TPMG was doing, there was a "mushroom cloud over his Honolulu headquarters."[24] Although Kaiser had "retired" from the active direction of the Kaiser Companies, the dynamic industrialist was still very much involved in business and especially medical care. In 1958, he had built a hospital on Waikiki Beach and recruited a medical staff in order to create a health plan in Hawaii that he intended to run by himself. Kaiser's program would be fraught with problems, some of which would be solved in 1960 only by firing the five physicians he had hired to run the Hawaii group.

The Honolulu Medical Center building, constructed under Kaiser's supervision, was also the source of major problems. The building itself was a luxurious facility. So luxurious, in fact, that before the hospital opened, the Kaiser-owned Hawaiian Village Hotel (still operating

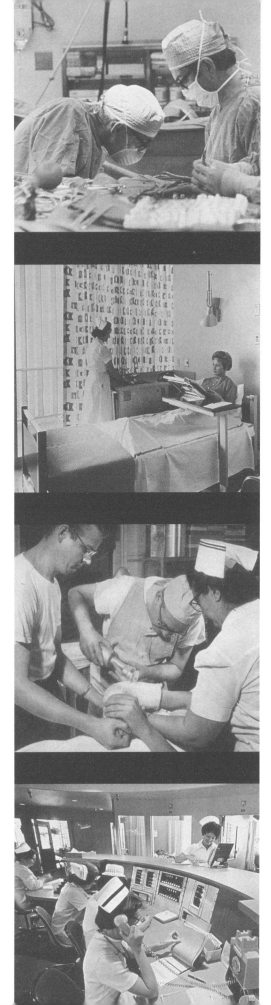

today as the Hilton Hawaiian Village) used it for guests when the hotel was overbooked. Reportedly, none of the uprooted guests complained about the switch.[25] But while the medical center may have made a great hotel, it didn't function very well as a hospital. Its central elevators were too small to hold a hospital gurney, the hallways were not air conditioned, the kitchen was inadequate and the outside corridors let in more water than they kept out. To make matters worse, Kaiser had insisted upon surfacing the hospital with lava rock, a practice forbidden by city code because the rock created a haven for rats. But the man known as 'Hurry up Henry' already had the first two floors of the hospital covered with lava rock before the planning authorities had a chance to protest.[26] Whether the rats took up residence or not, Henry Kaiser had his hands full in Hawaii when he received the news about The Permanente Medical Group — upstarts! — daring to venture to San Diego to start a competitive Health Plan.

Henry Kaiser wasn't the only one riled up by TPMG's expansion plans. By now, Ray Kay had decided that TPMG's independent operation in San Diego could jeopardize the entire Kaiser Permanente program. And what if SCPMG wanted to expand to San Diego in the future? The whole thing was starting to look like a very bad idea. "After much consideration we decided that the establishment of a separate health care program by the Northern California Medical Group [The Permanente Medical Group] in San Diego should be discouraged," said Ray Kay.[27] At this point, Kay went to Hawaii to talk with Henry Kaiser to see if they could solve the problem. Kaiser had a solution alright — fire all the TPMG physicians!

Such drastic action may well have been Henry Kaiser's intention when he returned to Northern California to handle the matter himself. In his excellent history of The Permanente Medical Group, John Smillie describes the meeting between Kaiser and Cecil Cutting, TPMG's Executive Director. "Kaiser stood looking out at Lake Merritt from the top floor of the Kaiser building," wrote Smillie. "Cutting approached him, but Kaiser refused to turn around, not even to a physician who had lived in his house for months during Bess

Kaiser's final illness 10 years earlier. 'Mr. Kaiser,' Cecil Cutting asked, 'would you really destroy this plan because of San Diego?' Kaiser replied that yes, indeed, he would."[28]

And that was that. In September 1961, TPMG abandoned its plans to set up a medical care program in San Diego and sold the Lake Murray Hospital to an outside group for a tidy profit of $203,895.

The prospect of truly expanding to San Diego would not emerge for another five years, until 1966, when SCPMG and the Kaiser Foundation Health Plan were approached by the San Diego Community Health Plan. This prepaid group was having financial problems and could no longer serve its members in the San Diego area. Ironically, the presence of this same prepaid group in San Diego had been a key reason that TPMG had decided to set up its own program in the same area, based on the Health Plan's belief that it was advantageous to have an existing prepaid group in a new area. Ideally, this existing group would already have educated the general population about the prepaid concept, so people would understand the Kaiser plan once it arrived. Now this same group was asking the Kaiser organization to take it over. "The Health Plan and I felt this was a natural expansion," said Ray Kay, "that it completed our program in this area, and that there were 30,000 or 40,000 members down there that really needed care."[29]

Ray Kay and a few members of SCPMG's Board of Directors were all for acquiring the San Diego assets which, in one of those strange coincidences, just happened to include the same Lake Murray Hospital briefly owned by TPMG in 1961. But most Board members, including Herman Weiner and T. Hart Baker (both of whom would go on to become SCPMG Medical Directors) were against branching out to San Diego. Why, they and others wanted to know, would the organization want to take on an insolvent prepaid health plan? Furthermore, the majority of Board members were concerned about having to use what they feared might be "inferior" doctors from the failed San Diego group. They were also concerned that it would be difficult to staff the new service area because SCPMG was barely keeping up with staffing needs in its existing

facilities. But Kay believed that none of these problems were insurmountable; besides that, the San Diego Community Health Plan was doing everything it could to facilitate the buyout. They promised a smooth transition and, most importantly, offered to absorb all financial losses involved in the takeover — along with existing debts.

Kay knew he needed Board approval to expand to San Diego and suspected he didn't have it. He asked for a straw vote to see if the Board was for the expansion or against it. The vote was against it. That's when Kay reminded everyone that the straw vote didn't count. But Kay knew the next vote would count, so he decided to take the Board members to San Diego to look over the operation he wanted to acquire. After the group had returned from their inspection trip, Kay called for a final vote. This time he won, but barely. The vote was 11 to 9. It was, said Kay, "the closest vote of the Board of Directors in my experience."[30]

And so in 1966, SCPMG expanded its service area to San Diego, at first working out of the hospitals and medical offices which had belonged to the San Diego Community Health Plan. SCPMG sent a group of "seasoned" physicians to work with the new medical group. This integration of "old" and "new" physicians was an SCPMG practice to ensure that the Group's methodologies and quality systems were implemented in a new area. Today the same practice is called 'passing on the culture of an organization.' In the case of San Diego, it would also be a way to evaluate the existing staff. "And though we gave every physician [from San Diego] an opportunity to demonstrate his ability," said Ray Kay, "it was clearly understood that only those who met our requirements would be retained. As a result, those who did not qualify dropped out; those we asked to remain have made real contributions."[31]

Under the leadership of Buck Wallin, who had also headed the programs in Harbor City and Bellflower, the San Diego program was successful even in its first year of operation. Plans were soon launched to build the Kaiser Permanente San Diego Medical Center. The Medical Center, which used the same design as the West Los Angeles Medical Center, would be opened in 1975.

REGIONALIZING MEDICAL SERVICES

With new facilities opening throughout Southern California, SCPMG began to realize that duplicating specialty services at each medical center was neither efficient nor cost-effective. It simply made more sense to regionalize services, to concentrate knowledgeable staff and advanced equipment in one or several medical centers only, not all of them. But, above all, regionalization was about quality of care. "Regionalization was initiated primarily to assure and maintain a high degree of quality and sophistication with effective quality control. Economy of operation was also anticipated and both of these objectives have been realized," wrote Ray Kay in his 1979 book.[32]

In 1966, laboratory services were regionalized in a Central Laboratory, under the direction of Dr. Jack Gordon, a highly respected and accomplished member of the Group. Initially, the plan called for each medical center to maintain its own lab to perform basic and emergency procedures only, and turn everything else over to the Central Lab located at the Los Angeles Medical Center. Samples were to be brought by courier from the other locations, and report slips returned via the same courier.

However, some lab personnel at the various medical centers soon began to resist the centralized lab concept, feeling it sapped the challenge and variety out of their own work. So a compromise was worked out to keep these skilled professionals satisfied and involved. Under the compromise, some specialized lab services would be regionalized at medical centers other than the LA Medical Center. For instance, the Bellflower Medical Center lab was set up to perform electrophoresis for the entire Region. An endocrinology laboratory, able to perform the most complex endocrine tests, was established at the Harbor City Medical Center. The Central Laboratory would continue to perform most of the chemistry, bacteriology, cytology, toxicology and other more specialized procedures. The compromise, which took human and professional pride factors into account, was a good one. It not only solved the immediate problem of employee satisfaction, it also helped develop good lab workers throughout the system.

Those who knew Jack Gordon were not surprised at his people-oriented solution. When Dr. Gordon resigned as Director of the Regional Laboratories in 1985, his personal and professional qualities were equally praised. From the SCPMG newsletter, *Partners News*, in April 1986: "When you talk to people who have known and worked with Dr. Gordon during his past 32 years with SCPMG, you immediately sense their intense admiration, respect, loyalty and affection for this man who has taught and led them. Through his leadership and dedication we now have the finest and largest laboratory system in the nation — and even in the world. But while the people who have known him mention his accomplishments, they more often focus on his human qualities and what it has meant to be associated with him. What are some of these qualities? First mentioned is his consideration and appreciation of the people whose lives he touches — from the patients who benefit from his skills to all the people who work with him. In his eyes, there are no unimportant jobs or people. He also has an uncanny ability to select people for their potential and infuse them with his philosophy of service and quality."

By regionalizing certain services and procedures, SCPMG was able to offer many services in-house that the Group had previously been performing at outside facilities. For example, from 1955 to 1960, Kaiser Permanente patients had been sent to the UCLA Medical Center for cardiac catheterization. In 1960, Dr. Peter Mahrer, an adult cardiologist, and Dr. Sam Sapin, SCPMG's first pediatric cardiologist, opened the Medical Group's own catheterization laboratory at the Los Angeles Medical Center. The two physicians assisted each other with both pediatric and adult cases and performed procedures about one day a week, in a regular X-ray room, on a fluoroscopic table. When Mahrer and Sapin transferred to Panorama City in 1962, the Cardiac Catheterization Lab moved with them and continued to serve as the Regional lab for both children and adults. In 1983, the lab would move back to its original home at the Los Angeles Medical Center, where it would become one of the largest and most respected facilities in the country. "We have pioneered outpatient cardiac catheterization," said Peter Mahrer in 1990, then Director of Regional Catheterization. "We were the first Group that did a large series and published it in the medical literature, and this has subsequently been accepted pretty much as the standard of care. Our laboratory has become nationally recognized and with that I have derived tremendous personal satisfaction from having been involved in developing this."[33]

In 1967 SCPMG opened a center for radiotherapy at the Los Angeles Medical Center, headed by Dr. Thomas Wolever. Before the center opened, the Medical Group had been using a nearby cobalt machine, staffed by the Medical Group's own radiotherapist and technicians.

As a result, when the center started service, a trained team was ready to serve patients referred from all Kaiser Permanente medical centers throughout Southern California. Since many treatments were given as part of a series running four to eight weeks, the medical care program made apartments available for patients who lived too far from the center to easily commute.

The success of these early efforts in regionalizing certain services would generate similar efforts in later years. Many of these special programs and services would be housed at the Los Angeles Medical Center, a relatively central location for Health Plan members around the Southland. Over time, the Sunset facility's concentration of specialists and advanced technologists would enable it to provide care comparable to any university medical center.

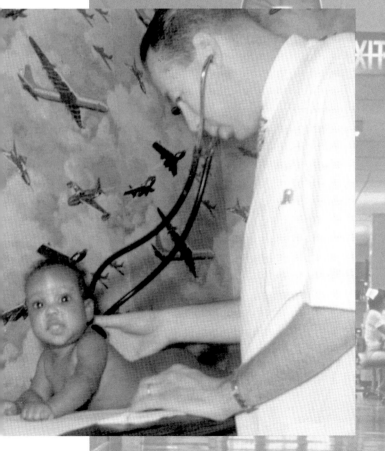

Sam Sapin, MD with patient

REACHING OUT TO THE COMMUNITY

As nonprofit entities, the Kaiser Permanente Hospitals and Health Plan made a commitment early on to provide various services free-of-charge to the communities they serve. Throughout the years, SCPMG would take a leading role in many of the programs and activities designed to improve the general well-being not only of Kaiser Permanente members but also of the community at large.

During the 1960s, the Southern California Region stepped up its efforts to provide services for low-income populations. In February 1964, the Region established the Kaiser Foundation Center for Child Psychiatry (later known as the Kaiser Foundation Parent-Child Guidance Center). SCPMG supported the project as part of the Group's desire to help prevent and treat emotional problems in families with a child under 12 years of age.

Services were made available to both Health Plan family members whose insurance did not cover this type of care and to other families in the greater LA area who were unable to afford such services. The broad range of services offered included individual and group therapy, family therapy and parent education.

In 1967, just two years after the Watts riots rocked Los Angeles, Kaiser Permanente stepped forward to open the Watts Counseling and Learning Center, headed by Bill Coggins. While the Center would not provide any medical services, it would provide much-needed educational and personal development programs for low-income, disadvantaged families living in the Watts community. Kaiser Foundation Health Plan membership was not required for children, from pre-school age through young adulthood, to receive counseling and

educational services, some of which were provided to acquaint young people with the possibilities of a career in health care.

In 1968, Dr. Harry Shragg and the Harbor City physicians launched a project to provide free, comprehensive health care to 100 low-income families who were being served by the government-funded Harbor City Parent Child Center. Several years later, the Southern California Region began caring for 500 indigent families near Fontana as part of a program financed by the Office of Equal Opportunity.

FAR LEFT TO RIGHT
Bill Coggins, founding director of the Watts Counseling and Learning Center, with student, at the dedication of the new building, 1977

Watts Counseling and Learning Center, late 1960s

Building site at 103rd and Success Streets

Day Camp Program picnic, early 1970s

Play yard in back with students, late 1970s

Nine children in the Pre-school program, early 1980s

AMENDING THE ARTICLES OF PARTNERSHIP

The 1960s would bring further modifications to the Articles of Partnership, SCPMG's key ruling document. Originally signed in 1953, the Articles of Partnership would be revised many times over the years as the Medical Group grew and matured.

During these early years, one of the biggest decisions to be made was exactly how large the SCPMG Board of Directors should be and who should be on it. In the first Articles of Partnership, the Board size had been set at six appointed permanent members (Drs. Raymond Kay, Frederick Scharles, Alvin Sanborn, Jack Hallatt, Herman Weiner and John Winkley) and four elected members (Drs. Rene Cailliet, Leonard Buck, Erwin Goldenberg and Charles Knerler). In the 1956–57 revision, the Board decided to replace the appointment of permanent individuals with the appointment of permanent positions. From then on, those holding the position of SCPMG Medical Director or Area Associate Medical Director would automatically become Board members, but would serve only as long as they held their administrative position.

The number of individuals elected to the Board was increased from the initial number of four, to one member for every thirty full-time physicians in the Group. A few years later, the apportionment of elected positions on the basis of numbers of full-time physicians would be replaced by a flexible system in which the Board re-evaluated apportionment yearly.

With the number of elected Board members now linked to the number of physicians in the Medical Group, the potential of having large Boards was a distinct possibility and some cause for concern. "There was much discussion as to the unwieldiness and loss of efficiency of a large Board, so a reduction in the number of elected representatives was considered," recalled Ray Kay. "However, in 1963, we finally agreed that although a large Board did result in a certain degree of inefficiency it was justified because of the value of increased representation, and the growth and the development of each individual Board member."[34]

The 1953 Articles of Partnership had also established at what point physicians could become partners in the Medical Group and this too would change over the years.

According to the first Articles of Partnership, physicians were eligible to become "junior" partners at the beginning of their third year with the Group and "senior" partners at the start of their sixth year. In the 1954–55 revision, the Group eliminated the distinction between junior and senior partners and made physicians eligible for partnership after three years with the Group. In a 1972 amendment, physicians became eligible for partnership after two years of service rather than three. [Eligibility for partnership changed back to three years in 1995.]

Initially, elevation to partnership status was based on receiving approval from a majority of the Board of Directors and three-fourths of all the partners. In the 1954–55 revision, partnership now required receiving a three-fourths vote from the Board of Directors as well as from all the partners. While all partners continued to vote on new partners throughout the 1960s, by the end of the decade it became obvious that the size of the Medical Group now made it impossible for partners to know physicians outside their area and judge their suitability for partnership. So in January 1969, an Amendment to the Articles of Partnership authorized election of a physician to partnership by a three-fourths vote of the Board of Directors and three-fourths of the partners in the area in which the candidate worked.

Physicians' working schedules and salaries were also set by the Articles of Partnership and these too would be amended at various times. In 1953, the work week had been set at five-and-a-half days, with two half days available for educational activities. In 1957, the partnership voted to make one of these half days available for unscheduled time. By 1960, however, with the sudden burst in membership, physicians were "invited" to work their unscheduled half day for a 10% increase in base compensation. It was understood that this arrangement would be in effect only as long as there was a real need for additional physicians' work time.[35]

The need for physicians to work during their unscheduled half day arose again in 1966. At the same time, SCPMG also decided it was necessary to increase starting salaries to remain competitive. So in 1967, to solve both problems, SCPMG increased the working time of new physicians and raised starting salaries by $400 per month. Of the $400, $200 per month would be paid to new physicians for working their unscheduled half day during their first three years; $100 a month was put into the base salary in place of profit previously shared during the first year; and the final $100 was part of a base salary increase planned for all physicians in the

Medical Group.[36] "We thus hoped to make more physician clinic time available by attracting more physicians with the higher salary and also by utilizing the new physician's unscheduled half day for patient care," said Ray Kay.[37]

However, the Group still needed more physician time, so it began encouraging partner physicians to work on their unscheduled half day by offering premium pay. Partner physicians who had been receiving a 10% increase in their base pay for voluntarily working their extra half day would now receive 12% for extra duty. In 1971, the 12% premium pay for extra duty would be extended to non-partners as well as partners.[38]

THE BRIDGE BUILDER

An old man, going a lone highway,
Came at the evening, cold and gray,
To a chasm, vast and deep and wide,
Through which was flowing a sullen tide.
The old man crossed in the twilight dim.
The sullen stream had no fears for him;
But he turned when he reached on the other side,
And built a bridge to span the tide.
"Old man" said a pilgrim near,
"You are wasting strength in building here.
Your journey will end with the ending day;
You never again must pass this way.
You have crossed the chasm, deep and wide,
Why build you the bridge at eventide?"
The builder lifted his old, gray head.
"Good friend, In the path I have come," he said,
"There followeth after me today
A youth whose feet must pass this way.
This chasm that has been as naught to me
To that fair-haired youth may a pitfall be.
He too must cross in the twilight dim;
Good friend; I am building this bridge for him."

— *Will Allen Dromgoole (1860–1934)*

IN MEMORIAM
Henry J. Kaiser

Henry J. Kaiser's funeral program, which included his favorite poem "The Bridge Builder"

THE DEATH OF HENRY J. KAISER

Henry John Kaiser, Sr. died in his sleep at age 85 on August 24, 1967 in Honolulu, Hawaii. He had loomed so large for so long that it seemed impossible that this powerful human dynamo could actually be gone.

Henry Kaiser was a man who tackled every project head on, who virtually willed a vast industrial empire into existence simply by the force of his personality. As an associate said, "Henry Kaiser is like a happy elephant. He smiles and leans against you. After a while, you know there's nothing left to do but move in the direction he's pushing."[39]

For most of his working life, Henry Kaiser was involved in huge, broad-reaching projects that affected millions of people worldwide. Kaiser Permanente historian Stephen A. Gilford captured Henry Kaiser's pervasive influence in the fifties and sixties best when he wrote of people driving Kaiser automobiles on freeways of Kaiser concrete, protected by Kaiser aluminum guardrails. These drivers might well be listening to a station in the Kaiser radio network as they drove to their home in a Kaiser Community Homes housing development. The walls and ceilings of that home would likely be made of Kaiser-brand wallboards made with Kaiser Gypsum; the driveway and foundation might well be Kaiser concrete made with Kaiser cement and Kaiser sand and gravel. The electric wires running into the home were undoubtedly made of Kaiser Aluminum, carrying electricity from one of the Kaiser-constructed dams. And of course, when they needed health care, they might very well be treated in a Kaiser Hospital.[40]

Perhaps Henry Kaiser, always the visionary, understood that his health care program would become his legacy. On his 85th birthday just months before he died, and while still in control of more than 90 companies worldwide, Kaiser told reporters, "Of all the things I've done, I expect only to be remembered for my hospitals. They're the things that are filling the people's greatest need — good health."[41] Kaiser's prophecy was correct. All that remains today of the once-vast Kaiser empire is the medical care program that bears his name. Within 20 years of his death, most of his companies, including the giants, Kaiser Aluminum, Kaiser Cement, and Kaiser Steel, had been sold. Although some companies would continue to operate under the Kaiser name, they no longer had any connection with Kaiser.

Ray Kay, who had often battled with Henry Kaiser, would remember him with fondness and respect. "Henry Kaiser felt strongly and he fought hard, but he and his people also listened," said Kay. "As a result, we developed a healthy, balanced working relationship. His appreciation and support of the Program were of enormous value and I'm sure he felt that the part he played in establishing the Kaiser Permanente program was his greatest contribution to society. And I think it has become his monument. We all respected and appreciated his imagination and vision, and we learned that if your objective is right, nothing can stop you."[42]

CHANGING OF THE GUARD

Nineteen sixty-nine would mark Ray Kay's final year as SCPMG's Medical Director. In 1970, he was succeeded by Dr. Herman Weiner. Although Ray Kay would step down as Medical Director, he would remain an integral part of SCPMG for another 21 years, serving as Director of Medical Manpower and also as medical coordinator of the Comprehensive Health Program at the Fontana Medical Center.

Ray Kay has been described as tough, feisty and aggressive — and he would undoubtedly agree. But these were exactly the qualities needed when he assumed the leadership of SCPMG when it was just a handful of physicians working out of a small rented space at the Rexall building in Los Angeles.

Ray Kay had been the right man for the job. He fought for SCPMG and refused to back down, whether doing battle with Henry Kaiser, union executives, medical society leaders or the partners in his own Group. Kay had a vision of what this Group could, and should, be. It was Kay who had insisted that SCPMG become, and remain, a partnership of physicians and not a corporation. It was Kay who insisted that only the very best candidates be invited to join the Group and, in the early days, he recruited and interviewed many of them himself.

As many people would say, the Southern California Region had truly been created in Ray Kay's shadow. It would be difficult to imagine the organization without his leadership, but the coming decades would bring new leaders to the fore who would help SCPMG meet some new challenges, that of increasing competition and government involvement.

CHAPTER FIVE

KAISER

PERMANENTE

MEDICAL CARE PROGRAM

THE 1970S . . . COMPETITION AND CONTROL

"The key challenge of the seventies was government involvement."

— *Irv Klitsner, MD*

Official acceptance of the six Kaiser Permanente regions as qualified HMOs under the HMO Act of 1973. Sidney Garfield, MD also received the LBJ Award for "Service to Humanity"

L-R: *T. Hart Baker, MD; Max Brown, Regional Manager for Texas; Edgar Kaiser; Joseph H. Califano (Sec. of HEW); Sidney Garfield, MD, Ladybird Johnson; John Carpener; Unidentified; Unidentified; Willard Reimers, MD, Medical Director of Denver; William Dung, MD, Medical Director of Hawaii; Sam Packer of Cleveland is in background*

October 27, 1977
St. Regis Hotel in New York City

THE GOVERNMENT STEPS IN

B Y the 1970s, the federal government was becoming extremely concerned about the alarming rise in health care costs, and with good reason. The government was now paying many medical bills through its Medicare and Medicaid programs, both initiated in the 1960s. The government's desire to control the cost of health care for these and other patients would lead to unprecedented legislation and regulation.

One piece of legislation passed in the 1970s to help control costs would have an enormous long-term impact on the entire Kaiser Permanente organization. This, of course, was the Health Maintenance Act, signed into law by President Richard Nixon on December 29, 1973. The HMO Act would thrust Kaiser Permanente and SCPMG into an increasingly regulated and competitive environment. This was something the organization had never really faced before, but from now on, competition and its accompanying challenges would be a fact of life.

SCPMG would begin confronting these and other challenges with two new Medical Directors.

NEW LEADERSHIP

The 1970s began with a major change for SCPMG. Ray Kay, the man who had shaped the Medical Group and guided it with a remarkably strong hand for two decades, was stepping down. Kay actually had no choice

in the matter. In 1969, he had turned 65, the mandatory retirement age for partners. Kay would continue with the Medical Group the way many retired partners do, as an employee, but in December 1969, Ray Kay's lengthy term as SCPMG's first Medical Director came to an end. SCPMG was about to transfer power to a new leader for the first time, and it would not be easy.

It began smoothly enough, with the selection of Dr. Herman Weiner as Ray Kay's successor. Herman Weiner took office in January 1970. He seemed a solid and logical choice for the job. Dr. Weiner had been with the Medical Group longer than almost anyone else. He'd been part of that small group of physicians working in the Rexall building on La Cienega who had cared for the Health Plan's very first members in Los Angeles. He had been one of the original thirteen senior partners who signed SCPMG's first Partnership Agreement and he was on SCPMG's first Board of Directors.

Weiner had always been one of Ray Kay's most trusted friends and colleagues and Kay depended on him. Kay had made Weiner and Dr. Frederick Scharles his two Associate Medical Directors and the threesome

often represented SCPMG at major policy meetings. In the mid-1950s, when the Permanente Medical Groups and the Kaiser organization fought over control of the medical care program, it was Kay, Weiner and Scharles who regularly traveled to Northern California on behalf of SCPMG. The three men were together for the summit conference at Henry Kaiser's Lake Tahoe estate when the future of the entire program hung in the balance. They helped craft the Tahoe Agreement in 1955 which grew out of that historic meeting and which helped reconcile some of the issues that had been tearing the organization apart. Kay, Weiner and Scharles served together on the Advisory Council which hammered out the first Medical Service Agreement in 1956.

As a result, Herman Weiner knew the inner workings of SCPMG and about all its contracts and agreements. He knew the top leaders in the Health Plan and Hospital entities. He knew how to work with the Kaiser organization. Perhaps the only thing he didn't know was how difficult it would be to follow in Ray Kay's footsteps. Although Ray Kay said that he "tried very hard to stay out of Herman Weiner's way," he didn't succeed. Kay found it difficult to fade into the background and let Weiner truly take over. "Ray Kay was a very strong figure and he wasn't about to disappear," recalled Dr. Sam Sapin. "I think that if Ray had been totally out of the picture and Herm Weiner was on his own that it would have been OK, but with Ray around, it made it very tough for him to do the job."[1]

The difficulties took a toll on Herman Weiner's health. He decided the best course of action would be to take a temporary leave of absence. The Board of Directors appointed Dr. T. Hart Baker to take his place temporarily. Dr. Weiner then returned for a few months, but in September 1971, retired as Medical Director. Less than a year later, he retired from the Medical Group itself. In October 1971, Hart Baker was elected as SCPMG's third Medical Director, a job he'd hold for the next ten years.

Hart Baker had joined the Medical Group in 1952, after completing his residency in Ob/Gyn at University Hospital in Little Rock, Arkansas. In 1953, he was named Chief of Ob/Gyn at the then-new Los Angeles Medical Center, where he created a highly acclaimed department and residency program. In 1968, he was appointed the Area Associate Medical Director for Los Angeles.

It's thought that many members of the Medical Group had voted for Hart Baker as SCPMG's next leader because they wanted to correct the perceived "controlling" style of Ray Kay. Certainly, the leadership style of the two men was markedly different. Whereas Kay was known as a forceful leader who "insisted upon running the organization down to the smallest detail," Baker was seen as a "benevolent grandfather" who would allow areas and departments to run with minimal interference.[2]

Just as Ray Kay had appointed two Associate Medical Directors (Drs. Herman Weiner and Fred Scharles), so would Dr. Baker. To assist him, Baker called on two of the Medical Group's most trusted leaders, Dr. Jim Roorda and Dr. Irv Klitsner.

Jim Roorda had joined SCPMG in November 1954 as an internist in the Harbor City area. He began working first in the medical offices in Long Beach, then moved over to the new Harbor City Medical Center

after its completion in 1957. Dr. Roorda transferred to the Bellflower Medical Center when it opened in 1965 and was appointed Area Associate Medical Director in Bellflower in 1968. A year later, Dr. Fred Scharles, one of Ray Kay's Associate Medical Directors, died and Kay asked Roorda to take over Scharles's job on the Regional level. So in 1969, Roorda joined the Kay administration as Associate Medical Director and also Secretary of the SCPMG Board of Directors. When Hart Baker took office, he asked Jim Roorda to stay on. Roorda's duties as Associate Medical Director included handling the Medical Group's medical/legal problems and working with the Health Plan on medical care issues such as patient complaints and requests for reimbursement for emergency care. Dr. Roorda continued serving as an Associate Medical Director until 1982 (when Dr. Frank Murray would become SCPMG Medical Director), but remained with the Regional office as the Secretary to the Board of Directors until he retired in 1987.

In 1974, Hart Baker tapped Irv Klitsner to serve as Associate Medical Director-at-Large, a new position that would make use of Klitsner's great skills as both clinician and administrator. Klitsner had been one of SCPMG's founding partners and leader of the Group's entry into the San Fernando Valley. In 1954, he'd opened the Valley's first medical office. He'd been directly involved in planning and building the Panorama City Medical Center and was the first Area Associate

Medical Director at Panorama City. As the new Associate Medical Director-at-Large, one of Klitsner's key roles was to serve as Medical Director in Hart Baker's absence. He also served as the liaison with the Chiefs of Services at the various medical centers and represented the Medical Group in two national organizations, the Group Health Association of America and the American Group Practice Association. Dr. Klitsner would continue as Associate Medical Director-at-Large until 1982 when he returned to full-time clinical practice in pediatrics at Panorama City. He then pursued his long-standing interest in adolescent medicine and founded the very first teenage clinic in the Southern California Region.

Although Dr. Baker had a somewhat laissez-faire leadership style, he would greatly influence SCPMG during the 1970s by creating an environment in which many programs could grow and flourish. When Hart Baker retired in December 1981, Irv Klitsner looked back on how Baker's guidance had changed the Medical Group. "He supported and encouraged innovations to improve our primary care through the development of better family practice departments and residency programs. And, because of the expansion of our specialized departments, the quality of our tertiary care has distinctly improved. We now have departments we didn't have before — plastic surgery for example — and other special departments, like cardiac surgery, have grown in size and prestige. Our radiation therapy department is now one of the best in the country. [. . .] Our yearly symposia draw specialists from throughout the medical community. We've continued to expand our residency programs and our school for the training of nurse anesthetists is one of the few such certified programs on the West Coast. Above all, Dr. Baker tried to find ways of maintaining and improving quality of care. Our doctors are better prepared than ever, as our educational programs have continued to expand and more residency programs have started. In everything he did, Dr. Baker tried to strengthen what he considered the basis of the success of our whole program — the delivery of quality medical care in a compassionate, personal manner. He demonstrated this dedication and

nobility of purpose as practicing physician and as a Medical Group leader."[3]

Two programs in particular were near and dear to Dr. Baker's heart and would benefit from his support — the Ob/Gyn house staff training program which he founded in 1955 (the Ob/Gyn symposium would be named in his honor in 1980) and the Kaiser Permanente Hospice Program.

Dr. Baker's Ob/Gyn residency program would lead to many similar programs in other departments. "I think we, along with our Northern California brethren, were probably the first HMO to start training interns and residents and fellows," noted Sam Sapin. About one-third of the trainees were then invited to join the Medical Group. "We don't hire all of the graduates," said Sapin. "We are very selective." Careful selection paid off. "Many of these people have since then become leaders in the Group, which I think is further evidence of the quality of the training that they got and the importance to us of this effort," said Sapin, who also noted that "having interns and residents and fellows around challenges the full-time physicians to keep up with them. I think that's a very important ingredient in ensuring quality care."[4] By 2003, SCPMG would offer 21 accredited residency and fellowship training programs and annually train more than 250 residents, plus 70 affiliated residents from UCLA, USC and other top programs.

Dr. Baker also nurtured the hospice program in Southern California which, in the 1970s, was still a relatively unknown concept in the United States. The modern hospice movement had begun in England with Dr. Cicely Saunders in 1967 when she opened St. Christopher's Hospice in the south of London. St. Christopher's is considered the first modern hospice. For her vision and contributions, Saunders would be made a Dame of the British Empire by Queen Elizabeth II. Dame Saunders' work and teachings inspired Florence Wald, then Dean of the Yale University School of Nursing, to open The Connecticut Hospice in 1974, the first hospice in America.

Aware of these efforts and of the pioneering work being done in England, Hart Baker sent Dr. George Espe and a study team to England in 1977. Baker wanted the team to explore the possibility of providing hospice care to Kaiser Permanente Health Plan members. Before long, Dr. Espe's team became convinced that hospice care could and should be available in Southern California. Espe's team helped develop the Kaiser Permanente Norwalk Hospice, underwritten in part by the National Cancer Institute. The Hospice offered home care instruction and visitation, as well as compassionate inpatient care for people in the final stage of illness. It would serve as the model for other hospice programs and services that would eventually be provided throughout the Region. "The Hospice Program doesn't touch that many people," said Baker, "but in terms of humane, progressive care, it's one of the best things we've done."[5]

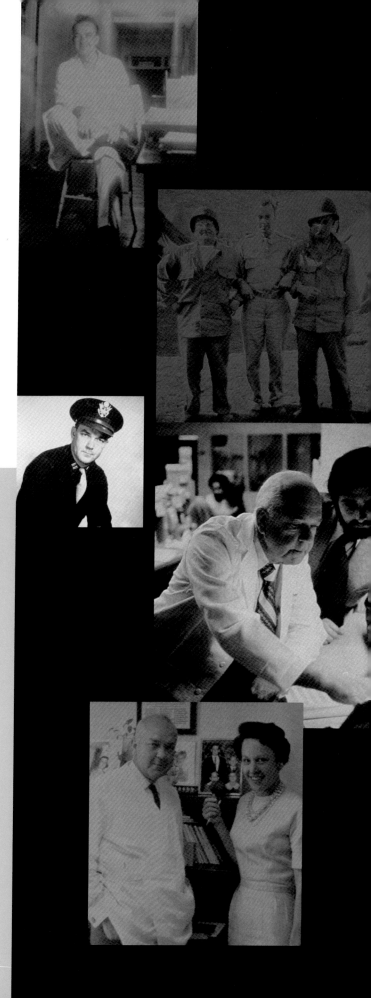

T. HART BAKER, MD

RIGHT, TOP TO BOTTOM
During medical school or internship
With his Army buddies in the 1940s
Formal Army portrait
Consulting

NO LONGER THE ONLY GAME IN TOWN

Before the mid-1970s, Kaiser Permanente had been the dominant player in prepaid health care in Southern California, and all of its other locations as well. But the passage of the HMO Act in 1973 would open the floodgates of competition, causing SCPMG some problems it had never experienced before.

The HMO Act grew out of the federal government's desire to do something about the alarming rise in health care costs. The idea behind the Act was for the government to offer grants and loans to help create Health Maintenance Organizations throughout the country. All these HMOs would then compete with each other, presumably on the basis of cost and quality. The government hoped this competitive environment would drive down the cost of health care.

In looking for a model for the HMO Act, Congress turned to the largest and most successful prepaid health care organization in America, Kaiser Permanente. Many thought it ironic that Kaiser Permanente, so vilified in its early years, was now viewed as worthy of emulation as a means to control health care costs and provide good service. Said Irv Klitsner: "We went from rejection, to tolerance, to acceptance, and now we were the fair-haired boy as a prototype."[6]

To make sure its standards became part of the HMO Act, Kaiser Permanente sent its own talented and knowledgeable representatives to Washington, D.C. to advise Congress and the Nixon Administration on drafting the new legislation. Those sent included Scott Fleming, a Kaiser Permanente attorney and Health Plan administrator who had been deeply involved with the program since the 1950s when he helped write the first

Medical Service Agreement. Fleming actually served in the Department of Health, Education, and Welfare (HEW) during the early 1970s as part of his assignment to help create the nation's new health maintenance strategy. Dr. John Smillie, from The Permanente Medical Group, also represented Kaiser Permanente in Washington for two years as he guided congressional leaders through the intricacies of formulating groundbreaking health care legislation. "He [Smillie] did a marvelous job of interacting with key congressional

Edward Green, MD

1969

Ray Kay retires as SCPMG's first Medical Director

1970

Herman Weiner becomes SCPMG's second Medical Director

people in helping them understand and shape the final legislation," said Frank Murray, who would become SCPMG Medical Director in 1982.[7] But the fact that Kaiser Permanente had served as the model for the HMO Act and helped shape its requirements did not mean that the organization would automatically become a federally-qualified HMO. Any organization that wanted to be an HMO, including Kaiser Permanente, had to first become fully compliant with the provisions of the HMO Act.

At first, the Permanente medical groups did not want Kaiser Permanente to become a qualified HMO. Becoming qualified meant meeting government-directed requirements, such as providing certain specialties and offering certain benefits; just the sort of outside control the medical groups had fought against for so long. But the Health Plan and Hospitals and many of the large employee member groups wanted Kaiser Permanente to become qualified.

And so the qualification period began, which for SCPMG included modifying the benefits package. "Much of the debate [at SCPMG Board meetings] related to what would be in or not be in the benefit package," said Murray, then Area Associate Medical Director in Harbor City and a Board member.[8] On some level, the Board had no choice in what benefits to offer in order for Kaiser Permanente to become a qualified HMO. The HMO Act specified that any provider must offer regular medical services, but also other services, including, for example, treatment for mental health problems. SCPMG had been offering a mental health benefit since 1961 in response to a request from the Retail Clerks Union, but it was, in Frank Murray's words, "a very skinny mental health benefit." Obviously, the mental health benefit would need to be increased if Kaiser Permanente were to qualify as an HMO.

Murray recalled the challenge of setting up a new department of psychiatry in the Harbor City Medical Center that would meet HMO Act requirements. "Prior to that time," said Murray, "we did not have a department of psychiatry as such. We had some mental health providers who were mainly psychiatric social workers and clinical psychologists as I recall. The department [in Harbor City] was run by a clinical psychologist. [. . .] There was a Regional Chief of Psychiatry, that is an MD who was a psychiatrist who was administratively overall responsible for the psychiatric services delivered to Health Plan members prior to the HMO Act. His name was Dr. Edward Green. He was a very capable person and a man who had done some very good things for our psychiatric program before the HMO Act. But he was also quite opinionated about how things should be done and also liked to control the psychiatric delivery process. That was somewhat in conflict with my own approach to things. I was an Area manager and I had my views about how I wanted those services delivered in my Area. [. . .] It was my intention to create a Chief of Service who was an MD. That was the way it was in all other medical disciplines, and as far as I was concerned, that was the way it ought to be in psychiatry. Dr. Green and I disagreed. He wanted a clinical psychologist to be in charge of the department. That would effectively mean that the doctors would be working for the clinical

1971

T. Hart Baker becomes SCPMG's third Medical Director

1974

West Los Angeles Medical Center opens

1975

San Diego Medical Center opens

1978

Program begins serving members in Orange County (Medical Center opens in Anaheim in 1979)

psychologist, and I said, 'No, that would not be the way I would have it organized in my Department of Psychiatry.' I made it clear to him that that decision, even though he was the Regional Chief of Psychiatry, was an Area decision that I would prevail on and not he. And I did. That anecdote shows you that we were treading new ground, treading new water and trying to find our way to effectively provide a service that we had not provided very well in the past."[9]

By 1977, the Southern California Region and all of Kaiser Permanente had completed the requirements to become a federally-qualified HMO. On October 27, 1977, Secretary of HEW Joseph Califano and the Managers of all six Kaiser Permanente Regions signed the necessary paperwork in New York City. It was official. Kaiser Permanente was an HMO. And so, it seemed, was everyone else.

The HMO Act had been designed to create numerous HMOs and it certainly achieved its goal in Southern California. Prior to the HMO Act, there were only one or two other prepaid health care programs in the Southland. "The old Ross-Loos prepaid health program actually had a longer history in Southern California than did Kaiser Permanente," recalled Frank Murray, "but they were much smaller and did not have nearly the favorable reputation that Kaiser Permanente did among employer groups."[10]

Although Kaiser Permanente would remain the dominant HMO, its status would be threatened in the 1980s when significant competition began to emerge. By 1981, there would be nearly nineteen HMOs in Southern California, all competing with Kaiser Permanente for many of the same members. For the first time in its history, the Southern California program experienced a marked decline in membership growth. When asked about the drop off, Murray had the numbers: "I believe that in 1979 or 80 we grew close to 100,000 members net. 1981 we grew 5,000."[11] From the late 70s on, competition would be a fact of life, affecting many of SCPMG's activities and decisions.

THE DEPARTMENT OF EDUCATION AND RESEARCH

In addition to requiring the Medical Group to offer certain specified services such as the mental health benefit, the HMO Act required providers to offer member health education, preventive medicine and high quality health care. SCPMG created a new Department of Education and Research to help meet these requirements.

Ray Kay had established a Department of Education and Research in 1963 to oversee all SCPMG research and education activities. Throughout the 60s, the program was run by Shirley Gach, a non-physician who, according to Sam Sapin, "did a wonderful job." But in 1972, Hart Baker decided that he wanted a physician to take over and expand the program to encompass some of the new government requirements he could see coming down the line.

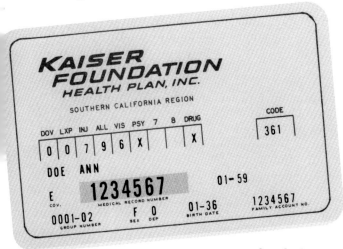

Sam Sapin, who had been Chief of Pediatrics in Panorama City for thirteen years, sent a note to Baker expressing interest. Sapin got the job and in January 1973 became SCPMG's first (and only) Regional Director of Education and Research. [The position would be eliminated in 1982 when Sapin was appointed to the newly-created position of Associate Medical Director of Clinical Services. The activities of the Department of Education and Research would be folded into the Department of Clinical Services.]

SCPMG'S FIRST FORMAL QUALITY ASSURANCE PROGRAMS

From its earliest days, SCPMG has had many built-in quality assurance mechanisms. As summed up by Sam Sapin, "It starts with the careful selection of physicians with a probationary period of two to three years before election to partnership. Chiefs of Service and Medical Directors are accountable for the quality of care and are able to award merit raises or withhold longevity salary increases, if necessary. There's mandatory continuing medical education for physicians. Physicians can easily consult with colleagues and specialists. There are no incentives to withhold appropriate care."[12] And at the very heart of group practice is an informal, but highly effective, form of physician peer review through the ongoing sharing of patients and medical records.

"My patient's medical record wasn't my record," said Frank Murray. "It was the patient's record, and it went wherever the patient went. If the patient saw one of my colleagues, went to the emergency room, had a surgical evaluation or procedure, whatever, that's where the record went. Everything I did and everything that everyone else did was there in front of me visibly to compare how they were doing with the patient's medical problems, as was I."[13]

"Sharing medical records automatically creates a continuous de facto process of peer review which is an important quality assurance mechanism," said Sapin. "This is a critical part of what we do in terms of quality of care. Because we practice in a 'goldfish bowl,' sharing patients and medical records, we know very quickly if somebody is not up to our standards, or if they need correction or improvement. It's an informal mechanism, but very, very effective."[14]

However, in the early 1970s, with the increasing government spending for medical care (especially Medicare and Medicaid), the government began demanding provider accountability and formal documentation of the quality of medical care delivered by health plans and physicians. One function of SCPMG's new Department of Education and Research was to assure compliance with the many new

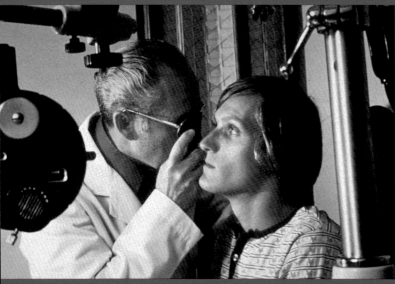
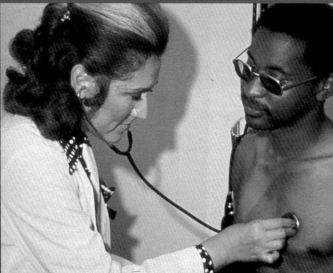
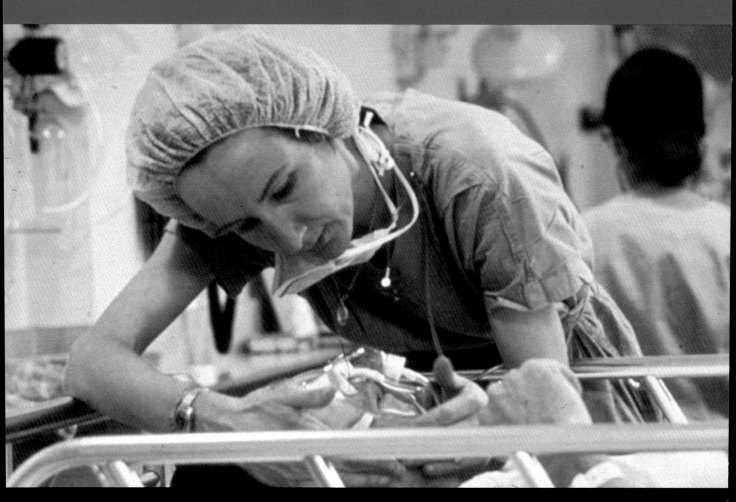

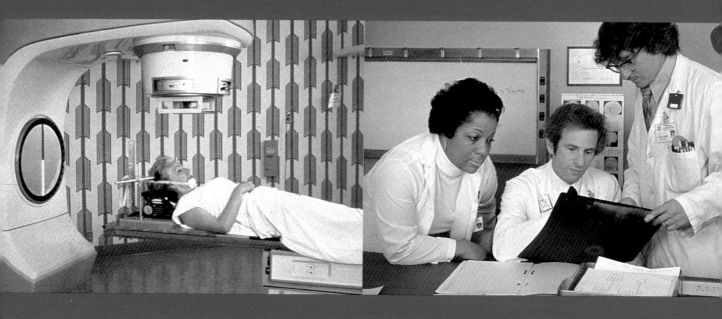

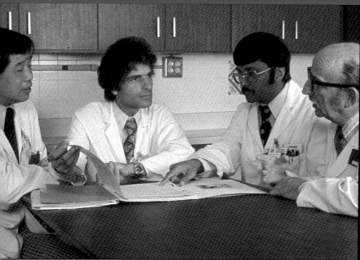

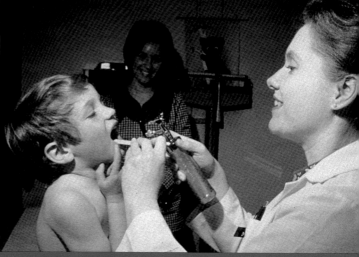

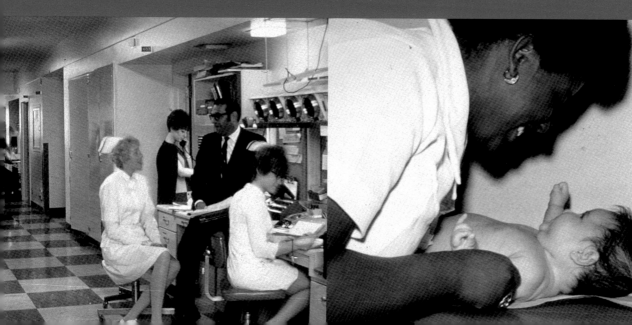

requirements regarding quality of care established by the California Department of Corporations (DOC), California Medical Association (CMA), Joint Commission of Accreditation of Hospitals (JCAH) and Professional Standards Review Organizations (PSROs, for Medicare and Medicaid patients.) All of these agencies required SCPMG to perform "medical audits" — retrospective, explicit criteria-based reviews of common diagnostic conditions and procedures, looking at the care provided (process) and outcomes.[15]

SCPMG launched its first "formal" quality assurance effort in 1973, with a then-unique regional medical auditing program. Under the new program, physician auditing committees were set up for four major specialties — Internal Medicine, Ob/Gyn, Pediatrics and Surgery. The committees selected the audit topics and appropriate process and outcome criteria for the topic. The criteria were ratified by the physicians in each department. The medical centers then audited the same topics at the same time using the same criteria. Participants compared results using an internal standard and took corrective action when appropriate. Re-audits were performed to demonstrate improvement.

SCPMG also conducted research studies in quality assessment and assurance from 1973 to 1976 as part of the Experimental Medical Care Review Organization (EMCRO) Project. This federally-funded grant was designed to develop feasible methods to measure and assure quality within an HMO setting — "real pioneering stuff" according to Sapin. Investigators used a modified medical audit model to statistically compare the levels of care in four medical centers (Los Angeles, Bellflower, Panorama City and Harbor City), then tested several methods to obtain and demonstrate improvement when indicated.

In 1978, an internal evaluation of the ongoing region-wide audit program and the EMCRO findings indicated a relatively low yield from these criteria-based studies that focused on common diagnoses and procedures. What's more, the cost of such studies was high. The California Medical Association and the Joint Commission of Accreditation of Hospitals came to the same conclusion and abandoned the classic audit

requirements. It seemed probable that patient care audits and other types of in-depth quality assurance studies would be more effective and cost-efficient if they focused on identified problem areas rather than diseases and procedures.

SCPMG would begin to focus on identified problem areas in 1980 with the development of a new two-level approach to quality assurance. The first level was designed to detect problems. Instead of looking at diseases and procedures as they had in the previous audits, investigators proposed monitoring fifty-six, mostly single, "indicators of quality." These fifty-six monitoring items would cover all components of health care, including both technical medical and consumer satisfaction. "We looked at various rates," said Sapin. "Like mortality rates for certain common conditions. We looked at complication and infection rates for certain surgical procedures. We looked at utilization rates. How long were people staying in the hospitals with various conditions? We looked at how often we were performing certain procedures such as C-sections. Were some medical centers performing more C-sections than others? We looked at immunization rates in pediatrics. Were all the medical centers immunizing their pediatric populations? Our monitoring data answered these questions."[16]

The second level of the new monitoring program was designed to resolve problems detected by the first level. If an immediate solution to a problem was apparent, appropriate corrective action would be implemented without further formal study. Potential problems generated a more in-depth investigation.

Regular monitoring reports were sent to Chiefs of Service, Medical Directors and administrators for their review and action. Sapin noted that the reports were delivered in a bright yellow folder, "because that was a more cheerful color and maybe wouldn't make them feel too depressed when they looked at their results."[17] According to Sapin, these monitoring reports proved to be more effective in generating quality improvement than did the previous classic medical audits.

These early quality assurance efforts would improve over time. "As we became more sophisticated over the years, from the early seventies to the eighties to now," said Frank Murray in 1993, "that [the audit process] has become a much more open and shared process, and a more effective process, so that we can tell in a generic way, not about specific doctors, but about specific medical problems, how we're doing compared to how we were doing before. The whole purpose today of quality assessment is for the purpose of making improvement, not [. . .] for identifying the bad apple. [. . .] We've become much more sophisticated over time in how well and how effectively we evaluate quality. We now have in place in my organization a process for both inpatient and outpatient quality assessment ongoing regularly over a wide array of activities."[18]

The Wellness Care-A-Van

MEMBER HEALTH EDUCATION

The HMO Act of 1973 required providers to offer programs in health education and preventive care to help keep people healthy and out of hospitals. The idea of preventive medicine was certainly nothing new to the Kaiser Permanente system. In fact, the whole system was focused on keeping people healthy rather than just treating illness. The tradition of preventive medicine went back as far as Sidney Garfield's days in the Mojave Desert when he often left his little hospital to visit construction sites and check for hazards that might injure "his" workers. He'd walked through aqueduct tunnels with a hammer to pull protruding nails. He'd worked with safety engineers on ways to protect workers from loose or falling rocks. On the Coulee Dam project, he'd seen the value of treating people early to help prevent diseases like pneumonia from becoming more serious or even fatal.

But Garfield believed that health care providers were not the only ones who could practice preventive medicine. He thought that people themselves could prevent serious illness or injury if they were taught how to do so. Garfield was a major proponent of preventive care through member education and as he often said, "Health education should not only be available, it should be unavoidable."

Although the Medical Group had many good preventive programs in place, it had not developed a strong member health education effort. The Group would soon take steps to remedy the situation, not just to meet HMO requirements but also to satisfy the desire of both Medical Group and Health Plan leaders to do an even better job of delivering preventive health care to members.

In 1976, SCPMG's Department of Education and Research hired Scott Simonds, PhD, a consultant from the University of Michigan, to review existing health education programs and services in the Southern California Region. Simonds found a bit of a hodgepodge. Some medical centers offered member education, some didn't. Those medical centers that did, offered what they wanted, with no real attempt to standardize programs throughout the Region. Simonds

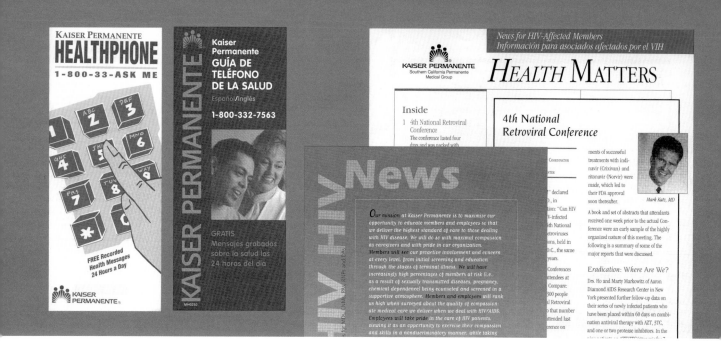

recommended creating both Regional- and Area-level member health education programs, a suggestion that would lead to the formation of the Southern California Departments of Health Education. He also recommended hiring a full-time Regional Coordinator for Health Education and proposed that all of the medical centers also have a Member Health Education Coordinator.

Among the first medical centers to hire Member Health Education Coordinators were Harbor City (Penny Wood, RN), Panorama City (Mei Ling Schwartz, MPH), Fontana (Nancy Kingston, MPH) and Los Angeles (Jean Harder, RN). Then in 1979, the Region hired Sigrid Deeds, PhD, as the first Regional Director of Member Health Education. Dr. Deeds, a nationally recognized health educator, had a tough time gaining acceptance for the program. Some medical directors remained reluctant to hire additional personnel for the kind of program Sigrid Deeds was proposing. But eventually Dr. Deeds was able to implement a health education program in each medical center and later helped design the Core Program for member health education. With the program under way, Dr. Deeds retired.

The idea of a Core Program had been proposed by Sam Sapin as part of an effort to ensure that members throughout the Region receive the same benefits and services. "In other words," said Sapin, "we wanted to ensure that members in Harbor City receive the same benefits as members in Panorama City, and so on. As

part of that, I thought all members should also be offered the same health education programs and we could do that by mandating that each medical center provide a Core Program. Medical centers could provide more if they wanted to, but they had to provide the Core Program, as a minimum."[19] Initially, some medical centers resisted the idea of offering a Core Program. But, recalled Sapin, "eventually all of the medical centers bought in and then the medical educators actually decided what the Core Program should be. These were the programs felt to be most important and would be most productive in terms of improving the care of patients [. . .]. We then developed an auditing system to make sure that the medical centers were actually delivering what they should be delivering. So that was a very important step forward in our organization."[20]

The Core Program initially offered a variety of patient education topic areas including diabetes, hypertension, kidney disease and peri-operative care. In 1988, the Core Program would be expanded to include HIV and hyperlipidemia. On January 1, 2003, the Core Program would be changed again to cover a uniform list of group health education programs, all provided at no charge to the members. Included in these groups of covered programs were Asthma/Chronic Obstructive Pulmonary Disease; Cardiovascular Disease, including Angina, Cholesterol, Hypertension, Post-myocardial Infarction, Congestive Heart Failure and Heart Health;

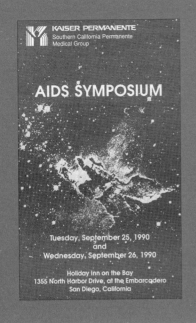

Diabetes; Perinatal, including Healthy Pregnancy, Breast-feeding, Newborn Care, Post-Partum Depression and Exercise/Nutrition; Healthier Living/Managing Ongoing Health Conditions; Smoking Cessation; Weight/Exercise/Nutrition Overview; Depression Overview; and Pathways to Stress Reduction/Stress Management.

While the Core Program would be at the heart of SCPMG's member health education efforts, there would be many other programs developed over the years to keep members healthy through education and innovative preventive health services. As Sidney Garfield had said, Kaiser Permanente would do its best to make health education not just available, but unavoidable.

In 1981, Panorama City would become the first medical center to open a Health Education Learning Center where Health Plan members could drop in at any time to obtain health education materials or view videos on virtually every medical condition. Later, several other medical centers, including Riverside, Fontana, and San Diego would also open Learning Centers as well as Health Stores where members could purchase materials.

In the mid-1980s, Sharon Conrow, then Manager, Department of Clinical Services, took the lead in developing a unique Wellness Care-A-Van which literally took the health education/preventive care show on the road. The 38-foot motor coach was custom designed for SCPMG and included three exam rooms. The van clocked thousands of miles traveling to many worksites

in Southern California as part of a comprehensive worksite wellness program designed to promote wellness through health education and selective testing. The program was available to all employees of the worksites visited, whether or not they were members of Kaiser Permanente. In addition to its important role in promoting wellness, the van served as an ideal way to promote a positive image of the organization, giving prospective members a firsthand experience with the "good people/good medicine" of Kaiser Permanente.

The Health Education Department produced a series of newsletters about specific health issues. The first of these was "HIV Health Matters" launched in 1991 with the help of Dr. Mark Katz, Regional Coordinator for HIV. For patients with diabetes, there was the diabetes newsletter, "Sweet Talk," started in 1999, under the direction of Dr. Fred Ziel from Woodland Hills.

The involvement of physicians such as Drs. Katz and Ziel in educational efforts was a common theme throughout the Medical Group. Over the years, many physicians had been, and would continue to be, instrumental in making health education an integral part of patient care.

Dr. Mike White, an Ob/Gyn from the San Diego Medical Service and a long-time proponent of member health education, started the Healthphone pilot project in 1976. For the first time, members could call in and hear a recorded health-related topic of their choosing. It was definitely an idea worth expanding. In 1978,

Dr. Tony Oppenheimer did just that, by leading an effort to bring the Healthphone program to the Los Angeles area. Healthphone services became even more accessible to members in 1987 when it went Region-wide with a toll-free number and 24/7 access. Today, the Healthphone is available to Kaiser Permanente members across the country, providing helpful information about topics ranging from Alzheimer's disease and baby care to mental wellness and first aid.

Starting in 2000, members would have yet another information source with the creation of KP Online. The new web site would give users access to in-depth health information and online services, including the ability to refill prescriptions and make appointments. Simply by logging on, members could research health conditions, take a personal health assessment and participate in online health discussions.

Among the Medical Group's most focused and enduring programs was a concerted effort to help members break the cigarette habit. For its part, the Health Education Department offered smoking cessation classes, started distributing "Independence from Smoking" kits in 1986 and launched a Regional Smoker's Helpline in 1988. In 1987, the Region banned smoking inside any Kaiser Permanente building, including all medical centers, medical offices, administrative offices and warehouses. At the time, people were still allowed to smoke at designated areas outside of the buildings, but many felt that allowing smoking in any area sent the wrong message. "We need to do all we can to get smokers to stop," said Dr. Gary Wong, who would become SCPMG's first Regional Physician Coordinator for Health Education, Health Promotion and Prevention in 2000. "Allowing smoking in specific areas has conveyed a mixed message that it is acceptable to smoke as long as it is somewhere else," said Wong. "We are unequivocal in our view that smoking is a dangerous habit."[21] In January 2000 the Region banned all smoking, both indoor and outdoor, at all Kaiser Permanente facilities. Kaiser Permanente would become the first major health care organization in the country to adopt such a policy.

Another dangerous habit that captured Medical Group attention was the failure of parents to use child safety seats in vehicles. This concern prompted an effort in the early 1980s to promote the use of child safety seats. In 1983, Health Education and the Ob/Gyn and Pediatric Departments in Panorama City prepared a brochure for all parents warning them about the risks of holding infants in cars or allowing their small children to move about freely. And that was just the beginning. The team also created a program to sell car safety seats at a reduced cost in the Panorama City Health Store and in the pharmacy. Every mom-to-be was taught about car seat safety and offered the same opportunity to purchase a car seat right at the medical center.

One of the Region's most unique health education programs was started by Dr. Guy Hartman, a pediatrician at the Fontana Medical Center. Dr. Hartman was particularly interested in teaching children about poisonous and toxic plants growing in Southern California. In 1967, he had created what he called The

Sinister Garden in front of the Fontana Medical Center. Filled with common poisonous plants, the garden helped children identify the kind of plants that could harm them. The unusual nature of the garden generated nationwide interest and focused attention on a previously-ignored hazard, especially for children. Dr. Hartman, who would become known as one of the foremost authorities on plant poisonings, also shared his expertise with the community, speaking to as many as 4,000 local and national groups and becoming "an ambassador of goodwill for the whole organization."

Guy Hartman, MD in The Sinister Garden at the Fontana Medical Center

OPENING THREE NEW MEDICAL CENTERS

Although the rise of competition promised some uncertain times to come, the 1970s remained steady and stable in terms of membership growth. At the end of 1970, there were just over 900,000 members in Southern California. There would be more than 1.5 million by the end of 1980.

Three new medical centers opened in the 1970s as part of an effort to expand service to a greater number of people over a wider geographic area. The West Los Angeles Medical Center, which had been in the planning and construction stages since 1968, finally opened in 1974. The San Diego Medical Center, also approved in the late 60s and based on the same design as West LA, opened in 1975. The 1970s would also mark the expansion of service to Orange County.

Since the Bellflower Medical Center had opened in 1965, it had served members in both the Bellflower area (southeast Los Angeles County) and in adjacent Orange County. But by the late 1970s, Orange County membership was on the rise, putting great pressure on Bellflower. Dr. T. Hart Baker, then SCPMG Medical Director, launched efforts to establish a new service area in Orange County and asked Dr. Larry Oates to become the Area's first Medical Director. Dr. Oates had joined SCPMG in San Diego in 1969. He served first as a staff physician in Internal Medicine, then Chief of Medicine and finally, as Assistant to the Area Associate Medical Director, Dr. Herb Sorenson.

Dr. Oates and his team began service to Orange County in 1978, working out of leased office space at Euclid and Romneya Streets in Anaheim. Some of the Anaheim physicians continued to hospitalize their patients at Bellflower, but also used Anaheim Memorial Hospital, just down the street from their medical offices. "Our initial service delivery was really based in community hospitals," recalled Larry Oates, "and we had no problems with this arrangement. Often, a community hospital has anxiety about Kaiser moving into their area, but it was quite clear that we weren't intending to purchase or take over their hospital, so we didn't meet a whole lot of resistance." Even so, the Permanente physicians in Anaheim wanted their own hospital. "You never could quite get the same impact using a community hospital that you could where you developed your own service," said Oates.[22]

Kaiser Permanente looked at a number of hospital facilities in Anaheim before choosing Canyon General Hospital, a doctor-owned facility on the verge of bankruptcy and up for sale. Kaiser Permanente bought it. The hospital officially opened as a Kaiser Foundation hospital on May 1, 1979.

For awhile, the hospital was rather unique in the Kaiser Permanente system in that it operated as a community hospital, largely out of necessity. "When we purchased the hospital," said Oates, "we suddenly had a great deal of capacity and so one of our initial strategies was to retain some of the community physicians who'd been using the hospital. This helped offset some of the costs of that facility as we were expanding the membership in Orange County. We took steps to ensure that the private physicians felt as welcome there as any Permanente physician." But not all community physicians were happy about the situation. As Oates later recalled, "there were a number of physicians who'd been against selling Canyon General to Kaiser, so they decided they would use other hospitals for their patients." Gradually, as the Orange County area grew, the hospital became less of a community hospital and more similar to the other hospitals in the Kaiser Permanente system which provided care almost exclusively to Health Plan members.

In speaking about Anaheim today, Larry Oates believes that the medical center created and retained a special patient-oriented culture, in large part because of its continuity of leadership. Two members of Oates' original management team, Martin Bauman (Chief of Internal Medicine) and Ken Bell (Chief of Ob/Gyn) would go on to succeed Larry Oates as Area Associate Medical Director. "For most of Anaheim's existence, there has been a continuity of the original management team up until Ken Bell retired in 2001," said Oates. "I think that fact had a significant impact on the culture of Anaheim today. All of us were very patient focused. We

were all trying to build a model there, in Orange County, that the rest of the organization could look to in terms of really caring about individuals as people. For instance, when Ken started the Ob/Gyn service, one of the things he did that was relatively unique at that time, was to use midwives and nurse practitioners. We believed that our patients would find that very appealing and they did." Patient satisfaction was also a top priority when new OB facilities were built as part of a hospital remodeling project. "We rebuilt a lot of labor/delivery units so that family members — dads, children, grandparents — could participate in the labor and delivery. We were one of the first areas in Southern California to really emphasize that," said Oates.

Oates points to this culture of patient-focused care, sustained by members of the original management team, as "flavoring the character of Anaheim."

Anaheim would also be home to a pilot project to test the feasibility of truly integrated medical center management. Traditionally, a medical center management team includes three individuals — a Medical Director and a Medical Group Administrator, both employed by the Medical Group, and a Hospital Administrator, employed by the Health Plan. Under the pilot project, Susan Garrison was appointed to fill the roles of both Hospital Administrator and Medical Group Administrator. "We started with a model where we really merged those two individuals into one position," said Oates, "because we wanted to blur the distinctions between the Health Plan and the Medical Group. We wanted to create a single-mindedness in terms of taking care of patients. We wanted to make sure that everyone knew they were working for the same team. We felt that structure would help us do that."

The pilot project would continue for seven years, until 1986 when Susan Garrison's position was split into the traditional Medical Group Administrator and Hospital Administrator roles. Susan Garrison then left to become the Hospital Administrator at Fontana and Pat Siegel was appointed Hospital Administrator in Orange County. Judy White was appointed Medical Group Administrator. "The expectation was that the other areas would gravitate toward the pilot project model or that the model would have to be given up. The other areas did not gravitate to the model and Orange County had to convert to the traditional model," said Judy White, Medical Group Administrator, Orange County Service Area. "People here were not happy about giving it up. They felt it had worked very well. Nevertheless, we work seamlessly in Orange County today, in part because of our collaborative early history and the vision of area founders Larry Oates and Susan Garrison."[23]

Today, the Anaheim Medical Center serves more than 346,000 members. Its special medical services provided to the Orange County area include the Rehabilitation Pavilion, with its state-of-the art Physical and Rehabilitation Medicine Program, and the Health Pavilion, dedicated to health education and health promotion. The Anaheim Medical Center is also home to one of the busiest emergency rooms in the county, providing emergency care to more than 44,000 people every year.

Anaheim Medical Center

San Diego Medical Center

T. HART BAKER RETIRES

Early in 1980 Hart Baker announced that he would retire as SCPMG Medical Director in December 1981. Baker suggested that the Medical Group select its next Medical Director during the first half of 1980 so that he and Baker could work together for the next year and a half. A period of overlap, during which the outgoing and incoming SCPMG Medical Directors work together, continues to this day.

After Dr. Baker's retirement in December 1981, he would return to his first love, clinical practice, at the new Anaheim Medical Center. Sadly, Dr. Baker would have only a few months to enjoy his return to medicine. He died in July 1982. At his funeral, he was eulogized as "a country doctor who saw the practice of medicine as selfless service to others, delivered with compassion and understanding." In later years, Dr. Baker would be remembered by Ray Kay as a "swell Chief of Service"

and by Dr. Oliver Goldsmith [SCPMG Medical Director from January 1994 to December 2003] as an "exquisite physician."

Hart Baker had led SCPMG through the 1970s with a gentle hand and had been a popular leader, but as his tenure drew to a close "there was a perception of drift and a demand for better coordination and better administration," said Dr. Lyal Asay in his history of the Fontana Medical Center. "This unrest resonated into a cacophony of demands for reform. Dr. Baker had overseen growth of the program through delegation but was now confronted by a crisis of control. [. . .] As a result of the crisis of control, Dr. Frank Murray was swept into office with the promise to institute that reform."[24]

And so, the reformation began.

1978 SCPMG Board of Directors

SEATED, L-R: *Kenneth Bell, MD, Ob/Gyn, Orange County; Irving Klitsner, MD, Regional Medical Director at Large; T. Hart Baker, MD, SCPMG Medical Director; Oliver Goldsmith, MD, Internal Medicine, West Los Angeles; Ester Fiszgop, Pediatrics, Bellflower; Frank Murray, MD, Medical Director, Harbor City*

STANDING, L-R: *James Roorda, Associate Medical Director & Secretary of SCPMG; David Myers, MD, Internal Medicine, West Los Angeles; Tada Sato, MD, Pediatrics, Fontana; Raymond Lesser, MD, Pediatrics, San Diego; Robert Schragg, MD, Medical Director, Panorama City; John Kondon, MD, Internal Medicine, Harbor City; Irwin Goldstein, MD, Pediatrics, Panorama City; Michael White, MD, Ob/Gyn, San Diego; Irving (Vincent) Roger, MD, Family Practice, Fontana; Lou Hahn, MD, Urology, Bellflower; Harry Shragg, MD, Medical Director, West Los Angeles; Frank Fletcher, MD, Family Practice, West Los Angeles; Benjamin Rubinstein, MD, Pediatrics, West Los Angeles; John Miles, MD, Head and Neck Surgery, Los Angeles; David Potyk, MD, SCPMG Board Member, Panorama City; Herb Sorenson, MD, Medical Director, San Diego; Irving Applebaum, MD, Surgery, Harbor City; Joel Satzman, MD, Orthopedics, Los Angeles; Charles Sadoff, MD, Medical Director, Los Angeles; Walt Groeber, MD, Medical Director, Fontana; Chester Haug, MD, Medical Director, Bellflower; Arthur Starr, MD, Urology, Los Angeles; Martin Bauman, MD, Medical Director, Orange County*

A TRIBUTE TO T. HART BAKER

His compassion and concern for all people were apparent. This concern was reflected in his continuing care of his patients, his guidance and encouragement of those who worked with him, his constant efforts to promote quality medical care, and his love of his friends and family. Our present outstanding Obstetrics and Gynecology Residency Program is a direct result of Dr. Baker's devotion to excellence in medical education. His leadership in the Hospice Program reflected his deep concern and respect for the humanity and dignity of all people. One of his goals was to have the Kaiser Permanente Program achieve the highest quality of medical care possible for its members. The example he provided and his dedication to the teaching of new physicians were living testimony to his ideals. The greatest tribute we can pay to Dr. T. Hart Baker is to continue in his dedication to the "delivery of quality medical care in a compassionate and personal manner."

— *Originally printed in* Partners News, *November 1982*

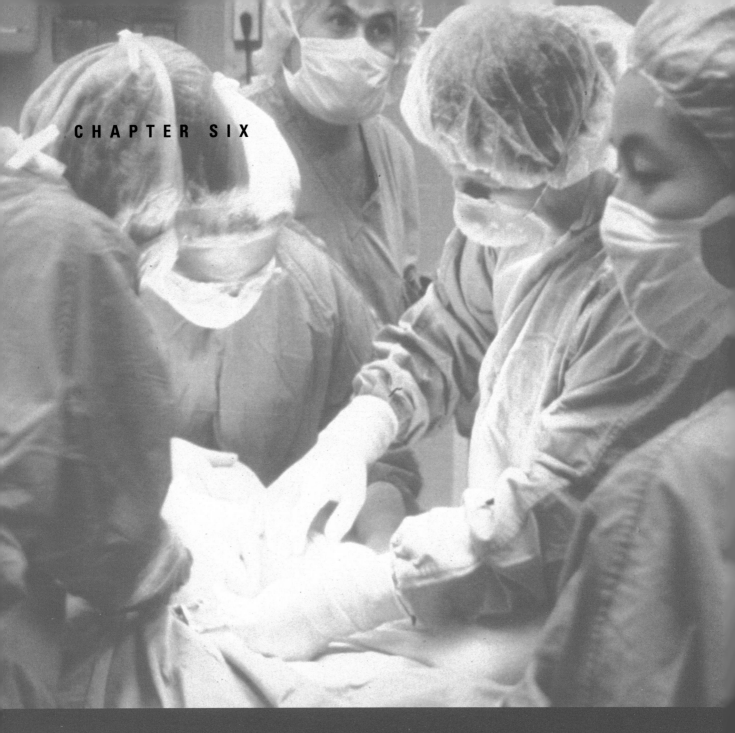

CHAPTER SIX

KAISER PERMANENTE
Kaiser Foundation
Hospitals

THE 1980S . . . YEARS OF TRANSITION

"There was no business orientation, none. As far as the Medical Group was concerned in those days, we were some two thousand doctors with two thousand autonomous practices."

— *Frank Murray, MD, SCPMG Medical Director, 1982 through 1993*

TRANSFORMATION

SCPMG would undergo a major transformation during the 1980s, from what many had called a "Mom and Pop" operation into a more sophisticated organization that relied more on business and data systems. This new approach was warranted by the Region's growing size and increasing complexity.

From the 1980s on, SCPMG would also face external pressures it had never faced before — intense competition, government requirements and regulation, increasingly-savvy consumers, a recessionary economy…and more. To complicate matters, as the decade began, the Health Plan and Medical Group found themselves in a relationship that had become "phenomenally bad."

In meeting these challenges, SCPMG would make some significant changes, particularly on the regional level. These changes would mark the evolution of SCPMG into the organization we know today.

Cardiac Surgery, Los Angeles Medical Center

NEW MEDICAL DIRECTOR...
NEW DIRECTION

In 1980, when Hart Baker announced that he planned
to retire in December 1981, SCPMG was already facing
some serious challenges. For the first time in its history,
the Southern California Region was experiencing a
marked decline in membership growth. Competition was
part of the cause. "Other HMOs were beginning to
adapt some of the things we had done to keep costs
down, and were beating us at our own game," said
Sam Sapin."[1]

Enrollment was also greatly affected by several
recession and recovery cycles in the local economy,
especially in the aerospace industry, one of the Region's
largest employers. At the time, no one knew if the
aerospace companies would be laying off 30,000
employees or hiring 30,000. Such fluctuations played
havoc with forecasting, facilities construction, staffing
and many other vital functions of the Region.
Meanwhile, rapidly escalating health care costs
continued to cloud the financial picture.[2]

It was in this environment that SCPMG selected a
new leader — Dr. Frank Murray.

Frank Murray had earned his medical degree in
1960, graduating summa cum laude from the University
of Wisconsin. After an internship and a three-year
residency in internal medicine at Milwaukee Hospital in
Wisconsin, he entered private practice in Wauvatose, a
Milwaukee suburb.

In February 1971, after about seven years in private
practice, Dr. Murray came out to California with his

FRANK MURRAY, MD

FAR LEFT, L-R
Frank Murray, MD, Irving Applebaum, MD,
John Kondon, MD, T. Hart Baker, MD

wife to attend a postgraduate medical course at USC in critical care management. While in the area, he stopped off to visit Neal Barber, an old friend who just happened to be an SCPMG physician in Harbor City. Dr. Barber told Frank Murray how happy he was with SCPMG and wondered if he'd like to look around the medical center and meet a few of the physicians. Murray would. "There were several things I was impressed with," recalled Murray when interviewed in 1993. "One, the doctors had high morale. They were happy. They seemed to be enjoying what they were doing. Two, they were good physicians. I could tell that from the kind of discussion we were having about patients they saw and the kinds of things they did. And three, I saw in the course of the conversation I had with several of them that there was a sense of social responsibility that I didn't feel at home."[3]

After returning to Wisconsin, Murray and his wife talked it over. Should he leave his practice and move to Southern California? The answer was yes, if there was a place for him in SCPMG. There was.

Murray joined the Medical Group on September 1, 1971 as a general internist at the Harbor City Medical Center. In 1976, he was selected as the new Area Associate Medical Director of the Harbor City Medical Center. When Dr. Baker announced his retirement in 1980, Murray urged two of his colleagues, Walter Groeber (Area Associate Medical Director in Fontana) and Herb Sorenson (Area Associate Medical Director in San Diego) to run for the job. Both physicians declined, but pressed Murray to try. "They were the only people, with the exception of some of the doctors at Harbor

City, who encouraged me to go for this job," recalled Murray. "I really was not known all that well in the organization. After all, I was at a very small hospital in a very small service area. I had been in my job a very short period of time. [. . .] I didn't have much of a track record."[4]

Yet Murray was prepared to take on SCPMG's top job. In 1979, Hart Baker had sent him to the advanced management program at the Harvard Business School. Baker had sent other SCPMG leaders, including himself and several Area Associate Medical Directors, to the same program. Providing management training for Medical Group leaders was a major turning point in SCPMG's history and continues today. Participation in the Harvard program marked the Group's growing recognition of the fact that if physicians were to run a complex Medical Group, they needed to have special management skills. The alternative was to have lay people making management decisions, something the Medical Group had always resisted, and always would. But with management training, physicians could not only manage their own Group, they could also evaluate the Health Plan's decisions and participate more fully in the "joint responsibility" established in the Medical Service Agreements.

Murray later described the program he and many others attended as a fair portion of "Harvard's MBA Program squashed down into about four months." What he learned there would open his eyes. "I saw the world in an entirely different way than I had seen it before going there," Murray recalled. "My horizons had broadened. I viewed the Medical Group and the Health Plan as having many deficiencies in business planning and business management and really believed that we were functioning very much like a fee-for-service world in the disguise of prepaid health care."[5]

Murray decided to run for the Medical Director's job on the platform that he could "put the right business systems in place and do the right thing for the organization and get it fixed."[6] He was ratified by the partnership on June 25, 1980, as Medical Director-elect. His first term would begin in January 1982.

As Drs. Murray and Baker began working together, preparing for the transition in leadership, the external pressures were mounting. Membership was growing, but failed to meet expectations. The federal government was in the process of enacting legislation to set maximum amounts for the care of Medicare patients. And there were all those HMOs, attempting to attract members by offering a Kaiser Permanente-like medical care program, at less cost.

As Murray had feared, SCPMG had plenty of problems of its own. He soon found "a low level of morale in the Medical Group with virtually no trust in administration, a lack of business systems in the Medical Group, no really clear vision or direction over how we would manage our financial and staffing resources."[7] Murray also saw that the Medical Group lacked the necessary recruiting functions and compensation programs to attract and retain the best physicians.

Frank Murray "soon realized that he must quickly regain control and set about to create a strong Regional office and apply the known principles of a centralized business structure," said Fontana physician Lyal Asay, in his excellent history of the Fontana Medical Center.[8]

NEW ADMINISTRATIVE STRUCTURE

One of Dr. Murray's first steps as Medical Director was to create a new administrative structure for the Region. The idea was to imbue the organization with a business orientation that would help the Medical Group function better in an increasingly competitive, cost-conscious environment.

The new structure proposed by Dr. Murray called for himself as SCPMG Medical Director and two Associate Medical Directors — one in charge of finance, one in charge of clinical services. This was a new concept. Although previous SCPMG Medical Directors had appointed Associate Medical Directors to assist them, the specific duties of these associates were not as clearly delineated as they would be now.

"The idea was that the financial associate medical director would take care of budgeting to ensure we had the resources to provide quality care and still come out well financially at the end of the year," said Sam Sapin. "And the clinical associate medical director had to make

sure we delivered the medical care that we were obligated to deliver to all the members, and do it in a responsible financial manner, looking carefully at the resources. These two medical directors were supposed to balance each other. The clinical director, making sure that he got the funds that he needed to provide quality of care and the financial director saying, 'Are you sure you need this? Is this the most cost-effective way to go?' That was the notion."[9] The Regional administrative structure that Dr. Murray put in place is still in place. "I think it has stood us well as an organization over time," said Murray when interviewed in 2003.

As evidence of Murray's haste to get SCPMG's financial house in order, his first appointment after he became Medical Director-elect was a physician with a flair for finance, Dr. Irwin Goldstein. Irwin Goldstein had joined the Medical Group in 1968 as a pediatrician in Panorama City. He quickly demonstrated that his skills were far more than just clinical, and that he had a particular interest in, and talent for, financial matters. In 1974, he was elected to the Board and, while on the Board, met Frank Murray, then Area Associate Medical Director at Harbor City. Murray, like everyone else, was impressed with Goldstein's quick mind and superb grasp of finance. After he was ratified as the new Medical Director, Murray appointed Goldstein as SCPMG's first Associate Medical Director and Physician Manager of Operations, a job he would hold until his retirement from SCPMG in December 2003. Murray later called his appointment of Irwin Goldstein "one of the very best things I did as Medical Director."[10]

In April 1982, Murray appointed Dr. Sam Sapin, one of SCPMG's pioneers, a highly-regarded pediatric cardiologist and former Chief of Pediatrics in Panorama City, as the Associate Medical Director of Clinical Services. Dr. Sapin would continue in the position until he retired in 1989, to be followed by Drs. Richard Rodriguez (1990–1992) and Les Zendle (1993–2003).

TOWARD FINANCIAL STABILITY

One of Frank Murray's first requests of Irwin Goldstein was to "fix the financial management system. It's got to get up to speed and start providing data to our managers that allows them to make management decisions."[11]

How would "fixing" the financial management system help?

For one, it would help track all sorts of activities including costly and often unnecessary outside referrals. "In some service areas there was absolutely no control or attention paid to services that were being referred into the community," said Murray. "Some doctors in some service areas referred heavily to academic institutions like UCLA for all kinds of procedures at the same time that we had the capability of providing it by our own physicians in another service area. We just paid the bills. As we sent people out to get care, we did not even tell the people we sent them to, the providers that gave them care, 'here's what we want you to do, and when you've done that, send us a report of your results and your statement, and that's all you're permitted to do.' We'd send some patients into the community in some areas, and if the doctor in the community decided he wanted another consultation, the patient might be referred to one of his colleagues, not a Permanente doctor, but somebody else. And the care they might give would be ongoing. We kept getting a series of bills, and we kept paying them. There was no management system in place to track outside care."[12] Dr. Goldstein would implement one.

Another problem. "When I took over, I think we had 1.6 million Health Plan members," said Murray. "So we were not small. We were a very large organization in terms of revenue as well. But we treated ourselves like a Mom and Pop operation. On medical technology [. . .] we did not take advantage of our size. Why should we buy electrocardiograph machines from five or six different vendors? Why should we buy very expensive radiologic equipment from three or four different vendors and not get the benefit of economies of scale, not only for the price we pay but also for the

maintenance contracts? Well, we weren't doing that. There was no conversation between Harbor City and Los Angeles or Los Angeles and San Diego on these things by the business administrators, by the physician administrators, by the chiefs of service, by anyone."[13]

Irwin Goldstein would put into effect the kind of business systems to solve these and many other problems that were threatening the financial stability of the Medical Group.

He put systems in place to help set operating budgets, to help set dues rates and to help the Group recruit and retain the best doctors, a big problem at the time. As Frank Murray recalled, "The Group was finding that many physicians would join the Group (especially those from cold climates!), work for a few years, take their boards and leave because someone in the community offered them a higher salary."[14]

Irwin Goldstein solved the physician recruitment and retention problem by formulating a process to offer the best competitive salaries and benefits of any HMO or managed care organization in the country.[15] "While the recruiters can be quite talented in doing what they're doing, it doesn't help if the compensation and the benefits aren't market based," said Goldstein in 2003. "We went about doing just that, where we have been able to have very low turnover now in the surgical specialties, which was not the case in the earlier years of the organization. We now pay what the market requires for those specialists."[16]

Dr. Goldstein proved to be an exceptionally talented financial manager. "He has made the most profound contribution to our Medical Group than anyone I can identify," said Dr. Oliver Goldsmith in 2002. "What has he done? If you think about financial stability of this program in Southern California you have to go down the path to Irwin Goldstein who more than any single person created that financial stability."[17]

COORDINATING CLINICAL SERVICES

On the clinical side, Sam Sapin believed that one of his key roles as the new Director of Clinical Services was to help change the Region from its then-current vertical structure to a more horizontal framework. In other words, Sapin wanted to break down the walls that the different service areas had built around themselves, and get everyone working together as the large, united Medical Group they were (or should have been).

"As I saw it," recalled Sapin, "we really had pretty much of a vertical structure, with each of the medical centers doing their own thing. They had their own medical director, the chiefs of service and physicians. They kind of functioned not totally autonomously, but to some extent autonomously and interpreting what benefits the members should be [given], often times a lot of duplication, doing the same services, delivering the same services, when it could have been done more efficiently by working together, of following another model. That was pretty much a vertical structure, and not too much communication back and forth and among the medical centers in terms of what people were doing."[18]

Sapin believed that a horizontal structure would be much stronger and, ultimately, to the advantage of the Medical Group. "This would mean more communication among the medical centers, more working together, more avoidance of duplication of effort, attempts to innovate, share new ideas, new experiences and try to bring people up to the highest level and work together and provide consultation."[19]

Throughout the 1980s, there would be many efforts to promote cooperation among medical centers. Key among them was the development of the Regional Chiefs of Service groups, whereby all of the Chiefs of Service in each specialty would meet on a regular basis. All the Chiefs of Pediatrics from all the medical centers would meet. All the Chiefs of Internal Medical from all of the medical centers would meet, and so on. "After each meeting of those groups there would be minutes and the minutes were sent to all of the medical directors,

all of the hospital administrators and Health Plan people so that everybody would know what the Chiefs were talking about, what their problems were, what plans they were having, what their needs were," said Sapin. "That structure is still ongoing and has been a very, very important element in our being able to deliver quality care, efficient care and make it comparable throughout the Region."[20]

Many Region-wide efforts were launched, each with a Regional Coordinator.

Some Region-wide programs and their coordinators were already in place, including Dr. Ray Kay as the Regional Coordinator of Medical Manpower; Dr. Rudy Brody as the Regional Coordinator of house staff training, charged with developing the intern and residency fellowships training programs; and Dr. Sheldon Wolf, a neurologist at the Los Angeles Medical Center, as coordinator of the research program. New Regional programs would be created as well. Dr. David Wirtschafter became the Regional Perinatal Coordinator. Dr. Les Zendle was appointed as Regional Coordinator for Elderly Health Care to meet Dr. Murray's request to do more about taking care of elderly Health Plan members. Dr. Jared Spotkov was appointed as the Regional AIDS Coordinator in response to the rising AIDS epidemic. As the field of genetics began to emerge, Dr. Diane Broome, followed by Dr. Harold Bass, became the Regional Genetics Coordinator. Dr. Mark Klau, an ENT specialist from Orange County, became the Regional Coordinator for Physicians' Continuing Medical Education.

When interviewed in 2002, Sam Sapin noted that some people had not been thrilled about the transition from the vertical to horizontal structure, that many resisted "going from their vertical situation where they pretty much could do a lot of things that they wanted to do." "There were some stormy days," said Sapin, "but I think we survived and the organization now is functioning much more in that [horizontal] fashion."[21]

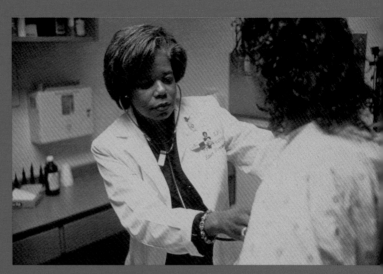

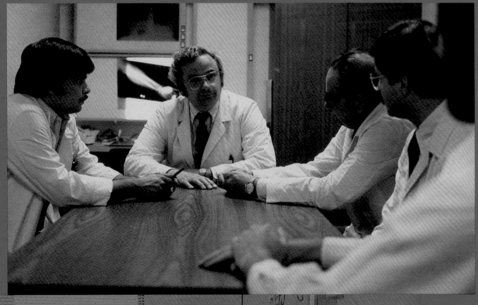

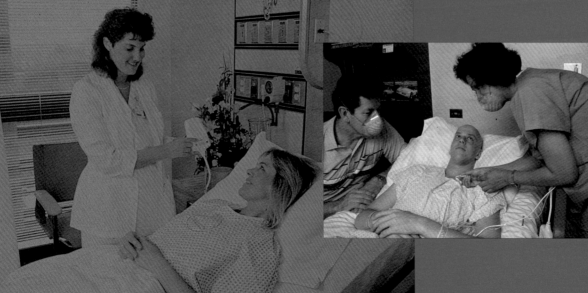

MENDING THE RELATIONSHIP WITH HEALTH PLAN

When Frank Murray became SCPMG Medical Director-elect, he was concerned about a lack of business systems, but he saw something else that concerned him as much, if not more. "Frankly the most severe piece of the challenges facing me was [. . .] the lack of trust and partnering that existed between Health Plan and the Southern California Permanente Medical Group in 1981. It was phenomenally bad."[22] The estrangement couldn't have come at a worse time. "I looked at that and I said with all of the competition we're facing and with the other challenges that are upon us, this is a real Pogoism," said Murray. "We've met the enemy and he is us."[23]

The deteriorating relationship had affected everything, not just between the Medical Group and Health Plan, but also within the Medical Group itself. Murray had seen the problems even before becoming Medical Director. "As a member of the Board," Murray recalled, "I began to see tremendous animosity between Health Plan and the Medical Group, lack of trust, no trust at all. The Medical Group's Board did not trust Dr. Baker and they did not trust Dr. Baker's partner, the Regional Manager [Carl Berner], and they didn't trust Health Plan in general, and they were open in their hostility about the level of rancor and unhappiness between them, and, by the way, it was not one-sided. Health Plan did not trust the Medical Group. So, it worked both ways. They were very suspicious about each other's motives and behavior."[24]

TOP
T. Hart Baker, MD and Carl Berner
MIDDLE
Frank Murray, MD and Hugh Jones
BOTTOM
Irwin Goldstein, MD and Frank Murray, MD

1982   1984

IMPORTANT DATES IN SCPMG'S HISTORY

Frank Murray becomes
SCPMG's fourth Medical
Director

Sidney Garfield dies on
December 29

Murray believed that the situation had reached the crisis stage. "I'm absolutely confident," he said, "that we either fix that or we don't have to worry about anything else, because we're not going to be in business very long."[25] In 1982, Murray took the lead in creating what he called the Medical Management Partnership between the Medical Group and Health Plan as a way to steady the rocky relationship and allow the Region to meet its many challenges (and the competition) with a united front.

Why was it so important to both the Medical Group and the Health Plan that they get along? "That is our strength," Murray would say; that partnership between Health Plan and the Medical Group. "[If] we truly work collegially with a shared body of knowledge, with purpose for those things that are in the best interest of the people we care for and the people who purchase our services, if we do that in an optimal fashion, there is no other structure in this country that can do that as effectively as us."[26]

Just as Murray believed that a good relationship between the Medical Group and the Health Plan could strengthen the program and make it even more attractive to purchasers, he feared that a poor relationship, particularly one in which the Health Plan dominated, could ruin it. Murray explained the dilemma: "You can't tell a doctor or a group of doctors over and over ad infinitum, 'Here's how you're going to do it and that's the only way you can do it. We'll pay you so long as you abide by our rules, but this is the way it's going to be.' You take away from the doctor, then, the ownership, the initiative, and focus on compliance and remuneration. It's a punitive approach that won't work forever. It cannot, and it will do things that will decrease morale, decrease quality of service, decrease technical quality of care, and I think ultimately will destroy the system."[27]

What Murray proposed to improve the Medical Group/Health Plan relationship was as much a cultural change as anything else; a change in the way in which SCPMG and the Health Plan worked together and related to each other. "I was willing to share information about staffing patterns, income, budgets, policies and procedures that affected the partnership agreement and our rules and regulations, and in return I expected the same kind of openness from Health Plan about any of their functions, their marketing functions, financial management functions, information services, and I wanted this to be a very open, free, blurred division line between the two organizations in order for us to work."[28] Murray seemed to be asking for a return to the commitment of joint responsibility that had grown out of the Tahoe Agreement in 1955, but that had gradually been eroded over the years.

Not everyone in the Medical Group supported Murray's approach. "Many of the people felt that that was taking too great a risk, that it may make us vulnerable if the other party [Health Plan] did not have the same point of view and they had information about you that could be used to disadvantage. There was no evidence that that would happen, you have to understand, but it was a presumption that it might happen."[29]

But Murray let it be known that the Medical Group would cooperate with the Health Plan — no question about it. Gradually, the broken relationship began to mend.

1986

Woodland Hills Medical Center opens

1988

Start of non-hospital-based service in Bakersfield

1989

Riverside Medical Center opens

"During the first six years of my time in office, I saw a totally different attitude and behavior develop between the Health Plan and the Medical Group in terms of cooperation and respect," said Murray. "And by the end of my second term now [1993], that has reached a place of high eminence. We are really doing well in that regard now. The level of cooperation, the quality of the people, is just outstanding."[30]

When Dr. Murray retired in December 1993, many cited the Medical Management Partnership as his most lasting legacy. The partnership "restored the respect and credibility of the Southern California Permanente Medical Group and helped establish it as the pre-eminent group in our Program, if not the country," said then-Georgia Regional Manager Richard Barnaby.[31] "We've truly become partners in every sense of the word," said Murray upon his retirement. "That makes me very proud."

Along with creating the Medical Management Partnership, Murray believed there was one more thing he could do to strengthen the Medical Group/Health Plan relationship and that was to revisit the Medical Service Agreement, the legal contract between SCPMG and the Health Plan. Did this agreement give equity to both sides? Was it fair to both sides? "Well, it wasn't," said Murray. "It was an old agreement that had not been dusted off since 1967. So we said, it's time to renegotiate this contract, and we did during 1981–82."[32] [The first Medical Service Agreement had been signed in 1956 following the Tahoe Conference. That Agreement went into effect on January 1, 1957, and would be periodically revised over the years.]

Murray and Irwin Goldstein led the effort to craft the new Medical Service Agreement to more clearly reflect the working relationship between SCPMG and the Health Plan. One of the new agreement's key benefits was that it specified formal procedures and processes for interaction on the part of Health Plan and Medical Group. For example, in the past, there was no formal requirement for the process used to prepare budgets; in the new agreement, this process would be clearly spelled out. The November 1982 issue of *Partners News*, the SCPMG Newsletter, called the new

Medical Service Agreement "the best, clearest and most equitable throughout the Kaiser Permanente Program."

The new agreement was approved by the SCPMG Board and by the Health Plan and signed on December 15, 1982. By renegotiating the Medical Service Agreement, "we ended up with a better relationship with the Health Plan but we also began to understand each other's needs and understand what it was going to take to make this relationship work," said Irwin Goldstein. "I believe it was quite successful because frankly the thing's been in a drawer for twenty years. Occasionally we've had reason to amend it but almost all of those reasons simply have been changes in law."[33] Murray was quick to credit Dr. Goldstein for his skill in crafting the new Agreement. "It's the best Medical Service Agreement that exists anywhere within the program," said Murray. "The credit goes to Irwin Goldstein."[34]

IMPROVING HOSPITAL UTILIZATION

In 1983, the federal government implemented something they called Diagnostic Related Groups in an effort to control costs for the Medicare Program. DRGs set the maximum amount the government would pay for various hospital procedures. Medicare claims for those procedures would be paid in that amount, regardless of the cost to the hospital. "You would think [that] would be of not a whole lot of importance to an organization like Kaiser Permanente which led the rest of the country in cost-effective inpatient care," said Frank Murray.

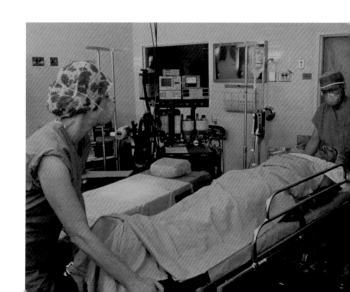

"We did not admit patients to the hospital unnecessarily."[35] Or at least that's what Murray thought until looking at inpatient care data in 1985. But there it was in black and white. The Southern California Region was averaging about 430 inpatient days per 1000 Health Plan members — a considerably higher rate than Murray was seeing in other areas.

"I looked at what Northern California Kaiser Permanente had, I looked at what some of our competitors had [. . .] and I was just absolutely frightened by the fact that we were being very far outperformed by our people in the North [. . .] and the community around us, our competitors, were rapidly closing on us," said Murray. "We were losing a distinctive competence." This, at the same time that the federal government was limiting payment via its DRGs. "That's an external pressure that I felt very dearly at the time," Murray recalled.[36]

Dr. Murray knew just how critical it was to reduce hospitalization days throughout the Region. He set a goal. "I forget the numbers," said Sam Sapin, "but it was a modest reduction in hospital days for the Region. Something like five or seven percent."[37] Murray announced that he would hold each Medical Director responsible if they didn't meet the goal. How to do it? Through a new program called the Appropriate Utilization of Resources.

Sam Sapin explained how it worked: "All of the hospitals were doing some utilization review at the time, but nobody was doing the same thing. We looked across the Region and picked out the best of all of the

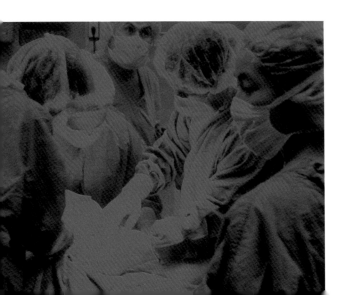

programs and put them together into a new program and said, 'This is the new model. This is what you all will be doing. This is how you do utilization review. These are the standards.' We even tried to set number of days that would be expected for various conditions. Then we had each medical center appoint a utilization review coordinator for the medical center. We got them all together, presented the plan to them, worked with them and then had them go to work. It was a Region-wide effort done in the same way, efficiently, because we were all doing the same thing, nobody was reinventing the wheel."[38]

In looking around the Region for what is now called "best practices," San Diego stood out as having relatively low utilization rates. Why? For one reason, San Diego had been performing same-day surgery since the 1960s when they started doing tonsillectomies and adenoidectomies in children on an outpatient basis. They would admit patients in the morning and send them home later that day. At the time, San Diego was pretty much alone in the practice. Most other medical centers were admitting patients the night before surgery, adding a day of hospitalization.

Sam Sapin, who had discovered San Diego's relatively low utilization rate in one of his medical audits, had previously tried to convince other medical centers to follow San Diego's model. Some agreed, but many refused to change their practice patterns. Time and again, Sapin would hear an excuse, "We can't get the anesthesiologist to come in at 6:00 in the morning. We don't have a room for patients to come in at 6:00 in the morning. We've got to admit them to the hospital, keep them overnight, do it the next day."[39] In Sapin's words, he "had no clout" to get them to change. But, as SCPMG Medical Director, Frank Murray did. In 1985, when it became obvious that reducing hospital days was a matter of survival, Frank Murray let it be known that "X number of surgeries will be same day and you're all going to do it."[40] So same-day operations became the practice in Southern California.

While Murray was insistent upon increasing the number of same-day operations, for the most part, he let physicians decide for themselves what other practices they would implement to reduce hospital days — as long as they did it and as long as they did not sacrifice quality of care. "They are just thinking of things I would never think of," said Murray in 1993. "But they saw the problem, they were empowered to create the solutions, and, by God, they're coming up with positive results. And I'm not telling them how to do it."[41]

"Lo and behold at the end of our year we exceeded our goal, reduction," said Sapin. "Then each year after that things went better and better. Ever since then utilization has been dropping. Of course the rest of the world has been doing the same thing. But at least we kept up and to a large extent that has enabled us to stay in business and meet the competition. But that's the first time that anybody's feet were held to the fire and Frank Murray called the medical directors and said, 'You're accountable now. You're going to have to do this.'"[42]

Utilization rates would continue to decline. When Murray was interviewed in 1993, he said, "We are today in some of our hospitals close to 200 patient days per 1000 health plan members. [. . .] it had been 430. That's a huge difference."[43]

NEW SERVICE AREAS

While Health Plan enrollment would slow down during the 1980s and become much more difficult to forecast, membership did grow. Even in those competitive times, the Health Plan continued to attract new member groups, pushing membership from just over 1.5 million at the end of 1980 to past the 2 million mark in 1990.

To serve these members, two new medical centers were opened in the 1980s — Woodland Hills in 1986 and Riverside in 1989. In 1988, a non-hospital-based service was started in Bakersfield.

EXPANDING TO WOODLAND HILLS

When the Panorama City Medical Center opened in 1962, most of the members it served lived in the eastern part of the San Fernando Valley where the medical center was located. During the 1960s, the Valley would experience tremendous population growth, especially in the western part of the Valley and in the contiguous Simi Valley and Thousand Oaks. "As the population grew, it became unacceptable for our patients in the West Valley to travel to Panorama City, so the first thing we did was put some clinical services in the West Valley," said Dr. Joseph Ruderman, who would become the West Valley's first Area Associate Medical Director in 1982.[44]

Expansion into the West Valley began in 1976 with the purchase of medical offices on Erwin Street in Woodland Hills. Erwin Street's first services were primarily in family practice and pediatrics. The Erwin Street Medical Offices are still in use today, primarily for internal medicine, psychiatry and physical medicine.

"After opening Erwin Street," recalled Ruderman, "we needed to find a place for internal medicine, Ob/Gyn and some of the surgical subspecialties. We also needed to expand our psychiatry and our CDRP — our drug recovery program." That need for more space and services in the West Valley would be met by the purchase of a six-story office building in Granada Hills. The Granada Hills building would continue serving West Valley members until it was destroyed in the 1994 earthquake.

RIGHT
Woodland Hills Medical Center

BACKGROUND
Woodland Hills Medical Center blueprint

Most of the West Valley patients continued to be hospitalized in Panorama City but, noted Ruderman, "we were overflowing in Panorama City, so we contracted with Granada Hills Hospital, next door to the Granada Hills Medical Offices, for some OR time, some beds and some emergency services." Kaiser Permanente also arranged for bed space at West Hills Hospital, then owned by Humana. "We had no problem working at Granada Hills Hospital," said Ruderman. "But when we went into West Hills, some local physicians objected because they could see the writing on the wall, especially when we started building our medical center. They realized they might lose patients. So there was some resistance to us being at West Hills, but we worked through it."

By the early 1980s, Kaiser Permanente had decided to build a hospital and medical center in Woodland Hills. They already owned some land, a seventeen-acre cornfield at the corner of De Soto and Burbank. The land had been part of the Warner Ranch, once owned by movie mogul Harry Warner of Warner Brothers Pictures. The land would become a master-planned business development known as Warner Center. When completed, Warner Center would be the heart of the Woodland Hills business community, home to a dynamic mix of high-tech companies, financial organizations, retail and restaurant facilities, excellent educational institutions and the new Kaiser Permanente Woodland Hills Medical Center.

In 1982, Dr. Ruderman was appointed the Area Associate Medical Director for the new West Valley Area. Joseph Ruderman had joined SCPMG in 1966, starting as a staff physician in internal medicine and rheumatology in Panorama City. He was appointed Chief of Medicine in Panorama City in 1976 and remained in that position until moving to Woodland Hills.

The design of the Woodland Hills Medical Center featured four towers — two outpatient towers and two hospital towers — as well as several smaller medical buildings. The campus would be built one structure at a time.

The first building, on the north side of the campus, was completed in 1983. The new building housed pediatrics, internal medicine, family practice, radiology and a pharmacy. The first outpatient tower was completed in 1985. "We put all of the subspecialists in there," noted Ruderman, "and opened a more extensive radiology department."

The first hospital tower opened in 1986, marking the end of reliance on Panorama City or local hospitals for bed space. "We now started hospitalizing all patients in

Woodland Hills," recalled Ruderman. "We brought the other subspecialties in, such as neurosurgery, plastic surgery, vascular surgery, neurology — services that hadn't been there before. We were now a complete service area." Woodland Hills was also asked to serve as the San Fernando Valley's tertiary center for neurosurgery, plastic surgery and neonatology. "Previously, patients in the Valley had to go to Sunset or West LA for those services," said Ruderman. "Now they were being offered at Woodland Hills."

The second outpatient tower opened in 1992. Two years later, a surgery center was opened in the same building. "This was the first free-standing surgery center run by SCPMG," said Ruderman.

The second hospital tower was completed, but has not been used for inpatient services. "We have not had to do that," said Ruderman. "Despite the growing population, the decrease in inpatient days and cutting edge use of outpatient services precluded the need to open more inpatient beds in the second tower." To date, the second hospital tower has been used for expanded imaging services and the Call Center.

Today, about 250 SCPMG physicians and a support staff of nearly 2,400 serve 165,000 Kaiser Permanente members in the West San Fernando Valley. Dr. Ruderman retired from SCPMG at the end of 1998, but continues to work several days a week at the Woodland Hills Medical Center as a rheumatologist.

REACHING OUT TO BAKERSFIELD

In 1987, Kaiser Permanente decided to expand the Southern California Region northward into Bakersfield. Frank Murray asked Joseph Ruderman, then Area Associate Medical Director in Woodland Hills, to oversee the start of service in Bakersfield while continuing his duties in Woodland Hills.

Ruderman's first step was to help draw up contracts with local hospitals, starting with Mercy, a Catholic Healthcare West Facility, and hire physicians from the community. "We knew that we would have to use all of Mercy's specialists to begin with," recalled Ruderman, "but we thought we would lose our distinctive care if we didn't have our own primary care physicians acting as personal physicians for our new members, with the added responsibility of directing their specialty care. I located four internists and a pediatrician in Bakersfield who had been practicing in the community. We hired them as Associate Permanente physicians, with the goal being full partnership where appropriate."[45]

The Medical Group hired Dr. Robert Mosser, then chairman of the Kern Medical Center's Department of Internal Medicine, to become the Physician-in-Charge. Dr. Mosser reported to Dr. Ruderman, who would continue to serve as mentor and supervisor for the new Bakersfield operation.

On January 18, 1988, Kaiser Permanente launched services in Bakersfield with the opening of medical offices on San Dimas Street, offering Internal Medicine, Family Practice, Pediatrics and Pharmacy. Administrative offices were located on California Avenue.

Growth in Bakersfield would be impressive, climbing from 4,000 to 13,000 members within the first year, then jumping to 36,000 members by the end of 1989. New medical offices were opened to keep pace with growth. In addition to opening the San Dimas Medical Offices in 1988 (renamed the Central Medical Offices in 1990), Kaiser Permanente opened the Stockdale Medical Offices in 1989 and leased medical offices at Physicians Plaza the same year. As membership reached 44,000 in 1990, the East Hills Medical Offices opened to provide the same services as the Stockdale offices. In 1992, services were expanded further by the opening of a

Gastrointestinal Laboratory (at East Hills) and an Ambulatory Conscious Sedation Center (at Physicians Plaza). These services had previously been provided to members at Kaiser Permanente–contracted facilities. Also in 1992, steadily growing membership led to the opening of the Ming Medical Offices, which would be doubled in size in 1999 to accommodate new services in adolescent medicine, women's health and radiology as well as an expanded health education department.

Through the mid-1990s, Bakersfield continued with local physician leadership reporting to Dr. Ruderman in Woodland Hills, but by then it was clear that Bakersfield needed Permanente leadership on site. "There was the desire to have a seasoned Permanente physician leader in Bakersfield because of the growth of the area," said Ann Ryder, who relocated to Kern County from West LA in 1993 as Medical Group Administrator. [46] "We had more than 50,000 members by then, so you're starting to have a serious commitment. Developing the Medical Group in Bakersfield became a clear priority of the Permanente partnership."

In January of 1996, Dr. Oliver Goldsmith, then SCPMG Medical Director, asked Dr. Thomas Godfrey to lead the Medical Group in Bakersfield. Godfrey had joined SCPMG in 1974 as a Family Practitioner at the Los Angeles Medical Center. In his years at Sunset, he served as a Chief of Service (Urgent Care) and as a Special Assistant to the Area Associate Medical Director from 1993 to 1996. As leader of the SCPMG physicians in Bakersfield (1996–1999), Godfrey was an Assistant to the SCPMG Medical Director, reporting directly to Oliver Goldsmith. In March 1999, several months after the untimely death of Dr. Fred Lapsys, LAMC Area Associate Medical Director, Dr. Godfrey was appointed to that position, where he remains today.

Dr. William Geckeler would follow Dr. Godfrey as the leader of the SCPMG physicians in Bakersfield. Bill Geckeler had joined the Medical Group in 1985 as a psychiatrist. He had served as Chief of Service in Psychiatry at the Riverside Medical Center, then as the Assistant to the Associate Medical Director of Clinical Services, where he was responsible for working with all

of the Chiefs of Service to execute projects and policies of the Medical Group.

On December 20, 2001, the SCPMG Board of Directors voted unanimously to make Kern County a full-fledged Medical Center, equal in status to the other Medical Centers in the Southern California Region. Bakersfield would now have voting representation on the Board consisting of two Elected Board Members and Bill Geckeler as Area Associate Medical Director.

Although Bakersfield would continue to use community hospitals, Ann Ryder would describe the arrangement as "a high maintenance model, requiring diligence on the part of the Permanente physicians, providers and staff to ensure that care meets Kaiser Permanente standards." Clearly the next major step for the Bakersfield/Kern County area is a hospital campus, currently slated for 2015.

Riverside Medical Center

PROVIDING SERVICE TO RIVERSIDE

Service to the Riverside community began as most service areas do, starting small then growing as needs dictate. Entry into Riverside began in the mid-1950s when the Fontana Medical Center set up a small medical office on Arlington Avenue with about six physicians. In 1963, the little group expanded by several physicians and moved from the Arlington location to the Van Buren Medical Offices, still in use today.

By 1972, there were a dozen providers in Riverside. Dr. Michael Neri, a Family Practitioner in Fontana, who had joined SCPMG in 1967, moved over to the Van Buren offices as Physician-in-Charge. Before joining SCPMG, Dr. Neri was living in Texas, working as a Family Practitioner with NASA during the Apollo program. He was recruited for the Medical Group by Hart Baker and Walt Groeber, then Area Associate Medical Director in Fontana. "They came to Houston to interview me," recalled Neri, "and I got excited about prepaid medicine, the fact that it was all-inclusive, that there was no billing. I joined the Group and I've been with it ever since."[47]

Since the mid-1950s, the Riverside physicians had been hospitalizing their patients at the Fontana Medical Center. This required the Riverside physicians to spend considerable time on the road traveling to Fontana to see their hospitalized patients, then returning to Riverside for regular office hours. Riverside physicians were literally meeting each other coming and going.

"One day," said Neri, "coming back from Fontana, I saw two of our cars going to Fontana and I said, 'this is awfully silly for all the physicians to be making rounds in a facility 18 miles away. Why don't we have one physician make rounds for everyone in the clinic.'" The idea was a winner and soon initiated a practice in Riverside known as "group rounding," in which only one physician made daily rounds for everyone, while the other physicians remained back in the medical offices to see patients. "This was the first time, to my knowledge, that group rounding took place in the Kaiser Permanente system," said Neri.

Riverside's next major step toward becoming a full-blown service area would occur in 1984. At the time, Fontana was serving about 240,000 patients, when the medical center was supposed to serve no more than 180,000. To provide some relief for Fontana, planners considered building new medical centers in Redlands and Ontario. But in taking a second look, the planners thought that growth in Riverside warranted a medical center there instead, so Riverside it would be.

In 1984, Kaiser Permanente purchased property on Magnolia Avenue in Riverside and made plans to build medical offices and a hospital on the site. The schedule called for the medical offices to be completed in 1987 and for the hospital to open in 1989. Dr. Neri was named Area Associate Medical Director-elect of the new Riverside area. According to Neri, "the Region was so anxious to get us started here that we didn't want to go through the usual design process of creating a new hospital, so we took the plans of Woodland Hills, just as they were." Soon, the mirror image of Woodland Hills was going up in Riverside.

Before the new medical offices and hospital opened, the Riverside physicians needed several things — more space for medical offices and a local hospital to use before their own was completed. The medical office problem was solved by leasing a building on Magnolia Avenue, several blocks from the new medical office site. To solve the problem of where to hospitalize patients, the Riverside physicians first went to Community Hospital to see if some arrangement could be made. The hospital administrators liked the idea of accommodating the SCPMG physicians, but the hospital's medical staff opposed it. "The Community Hospital medical staff was concerned that we were potentially a big player," recalled Neri, "and that by assisting us, it would only create a situation where some of their patients might transfer over into our Health Plan once we got our own hospital." Neri then went to Parkview Hospital. Figuring he'd run into the same opposition he'd seen from the Community Hospital medical staff, Neri asked to meet with the Parkview medical staff board. "I presented a proposal to them," said Neri, "that we would put our patients in the hospital, but we would use their physicians for laboratory, radiology, and for consultation in internal medicine. We agreed on some prices and the Parkview physicians approved the plan. They were very, very supportive."

The arrangement with Parkview continued until the Riverside hospital opened its doors in 1989, right on schedule. "In 1984," recalled Neri, "we had said we would have a hospital on site in five years. We predicted we would open on September 11, 1989 at 8:00 AM, that we would deliver about eight babies that day and that we would have twelve surgeries scheduled. And that's exactly what we did. We hit it dead on." Today, the Riverside area serves about 223,000 Health Plan members. Dr. Neri continued to serve as Area Associate Medical Director at Riverside until his retirement in December 2003.

REGIONALIZING MORE MEDICAL SERVICES

By the 1980s, a number of services such as the laboratory, cardiac catheterization and radiotherapy had been "centralized," most often in one medical center, sometimes in several.

It certainly made economic sense to concentrate expensive high-tech equipment and specialized staff in one location. It also made sense in terms of quality of care. "It's just a matter of doing things over and over — you get better and better," said Frank Murray. "It's no big secret. I certainly would never have cardiac surgery in a place that did 50 cases a year. And yet, you know, there are hospitals all over the country that do between 50 and 200 a year. I certainly am not going to have my surgery done in a place like that. I will go where they have 1000, 2000, a staff of folks who know from day to day, every day, everything that can happen, because they will deliver and do it right."[48]

Many specialized services were housed at the Los Angeles Medical Center, which provided Health Plan members throughout Southern California with access to the same level of specialized care they'd find at any university medical center. In 1981, the Sunset facility opened a Bone Marrow Transplantation Unit. At the time, the unit was only one of four in the Los Angeles area and one of the first such facilities in the country to be established outside a university or research setting. In 1983, Sunset's Neonatal Intensive Care Unit opened with a team of neonatal care specialists and round-the-clock nursing care to give premature babies the best possible start in life. A year later, Sunset opened the Regional Oncology Center and Medical Office Building, offering "high technology with a human touch." The new facility provided a completely self-contained center to treat cancer patients with the largest concentration of radiation therapy services on the West Coast. The same year, the LA Medical Center expanded its open-heart surgery unit which featured some of the most highly sophisticated, computerized monitoring systems in the country. Sunset would also become the Region's focal point for many other specialized services, including organ transplants and a cochlear implant program for hearing-impaired patients.

Perinatal services were also regionalized in the 1980s in direct response to a study of perinatal mortality done in the late 1970s. The study had looked at perinatal mortality in hospitals throughout California and showed that some Kaiser Permanente hospitals in Southern California had relatively high mortality rates. Hart Baker, SCPMG Medical Director at the time, put together a group of obstetricians, neonatologists, and pediatricians to look at how the Medical Group delivered perinatal services and how it could improve its outcomes.

The team studying perinatal services presented its findings to Hart Baker and Frank Murray, then coming on board as Medical Director-elect. Their recommendations included hiring a Regional Perinatal Coordinator. Murray, who had assumed responsibility for the project, asked Brian Saunders, then Chief of Pediatrics in San Diego, to run the program. Saunders agreed to take over the job for a year. Towards the end of Dr. Saunders' service, Murray brought in Dr. David Wirtschafter from the University of Alabama, in Murray's words, "an absolutely superb neonatologist and clinician."

It would be Murray's job to introduce this Regional plan for the delivery of perinatal services. "Believe me," said Murray, "it was not an easy thing to implement because it meant changing physician behavior and allocating staffing and other resources in strategic sites throughout our hospital system where high volume perinatal care was being rendered [. . .] and taking that authority away from other hospitals because they now needed to refer their care for their services to the subregionalized functions. That was probably the very first thing I ever did in my role as Medical Director to significantly alter doctors' patterns of practice — saying to some of our pediatricians, some of our neonatologists, 'No, you may not take care of 1,000 gram babies in your hospital. They will be referred to this hospital over here. All of your care will be given by a process in which we will transfer either the baby and mother, or the baby after the baby is born, to this other

place that has higher volume and where, because of the higher volume, we will gain the expertise in delivering that kind of care more proficiently.'"[49]

But concentrating perinatal services in selected medical centers would produce the desired results. As Frank Murray recalled with justifiable pride, "we went from that circumstance in the late 1970s of having some of our hospitals as low performers to being the best in the state."[50]

THE DEATH OF SIDNEY GARFIELD

Sidney Garfield died in his sleep in the early morning of December 29, 1984 at his home in Orinda, California. He was 78 years old. It had been almost 50 years since Sidney Garfield and Ray Kay had been at the LA County Hospital together, dreaming about creating a group medical practice. Both men would live to see their dream come true, and then some.

Dr. Garfield is rightly credited as the co-founder [with Henry Kaiser] of the Kaiser Permanente Medical Care Program, but he was always quick to point out that the program's creation "was not planned, it just happened." In a way, that was true. Sidney Garfield did not set out to revolutionize health care delivery in America. His agreement to accept Harold Hatch's idea for prepayment in 1934 had less to do with a master plan than with saving his little hospital in the desert. But Sidney Garfield made prepaid group medical care work, and work so well that he attracted the attention of Henry Kaiser.

Although the Kaiser Permanente program is often regarded as Henry Kaiser's legacy, it is Sidney Garfield's legacy too. In fact, Kaiser Permanente historian Steve Gilford is convinced the program would not have survived after World War II if not for Sidney Garfield's commitment and intervention. Gilford also credits Ray Kay, from SCPMG, and Morris Collen and Cecil Cutting, from TPMG, with the program's survival.

The Kaiser Permanente program was, in many ways, a product of World War II; a program for the 200,000 workers in Henry Kaiser's wartime industries — shipbuilding in Richmond and in the Pacific Northwest;

FRIENDS REMEMBER SIDNEY GARFIELD

"To him, good care of the patient was the ultimate objective of the program," says Raymond Kay, MD, one of the early Kaiser Permanente physicians and a close friend of Dr. Garfield. "The program that he developed is evidence of his imagination, determination, and administrative ability.

"From his early days of training, Dr. Garfield recognized the great value to both the patient and the doctor of having a group of doctors sharing the responsibility of the welfare of the patient," he recalls.

"To those who've worked with him, he was a warm, considerate, and inspiring man. An individual who could never do anything unkind or unfair," said Dr. Kay.

"He was one of the first people who recruited me," said Irving Klitsner, MD, Panorama City Medical Center, of his association with Dr. Garfield. "I was impressed by the caliber of his person and his interest in doing what's best for the patients.

"I remember I spent a year in Northern California, around 1950, just bulling with him (and some of the other early physicians), just talking with him and finding out if we all believed in the same things, the same philosophy of delivering health care. We found out that we all did agree," he said.

"There was one speech, years ago, to the medical directors — about the time everybody was calling us a bunch of communists — when he (Dr. Garfield) wanted us to remember three points that I'll never forget," says Dr. Klitsner. "One, keep your eyes on the stars — meaning that there's nothing beyond your reach if you're sincere about your goals and you're willing to put forth the effort to get there.

"Two, keep your arms around each other — your colleagues are your friends. Stick together, have sensitivity about their problems. And three, keep your hands on your pocketbook — keep expenses, costs down. Put something away each year (from your budget) so if you need equipment, you'll have it. That helped us all out when times were tough and we were all renegades in medicine."

— *Originally printed in* Coverage, *February 1985*

Sidney Garfield, MD and Ray Kay, MD

steel manufacture in Fontana. "Taken in its entirety," said John Smillie, "it was the largest civilian prepaid medical program ever achieved in American medical history."[51] And then the war ended.

War's end brought many defense-related industries to a halt and the Kaiser companies were no exception. The massive Kaiser shipyards, which had been rolling out a ship every few days, closed. The 90,000 workers at Richmond dropped to 13,000. The Medical Group in Northern California plummeted from 74 physicians to a mere dozen. The Permanente Foundation was considering closing the program down for good.

But Sidney Garfield wanted the program to continue and succeed. He believed the way to make that happen was to offer prepaid group medical care to the general public, whereas before it had only been offered to Kaiser employees. Garfield and Cecil Cutting took the idea of going public to Eugene Trefethen, Henry Kaiser's long-time advisor and the man upon whom Kaiser depended for many organizational decisions. Trefethen saw the Garfield/Cutting suggestion as a way to continue medical coverage for the remaining Kaiser workers, and so he agreed. In September 1945, as massive layoffs began in the shipyards and in the Fontana steel mill, the Permanente Health Plan, a nonprofit trust, was established to offer medical coverage to the public.[52] This step to go public marks the beginning of the Kaiser Permanente system as we know it today.

In the post-war years, Garfield would be the heart and soul of the program. The Medical Groups, the hospitals, and the Health Plan, while legally distinct, operated as a single organizational unit under Garfield's direction. In later years, his role would change and even diminish, but for many years "Garfield's continuing presence as an administrator, as liaison to Henry Kaiser, as innovator and public spokesperson, provided for the program and its core physicians a leader around whom they could rally as they struggled to implement their innovative health plan."[53]

Just as the Kaiser Permanente program itself owes its existence in large part to Sidney Garfield, so do the Permanente Medical Groups in both Northern and Southern California. After the war, both Medical Groups were still "owned" by Sidney Garfield and all personnel, including physicians, remained Garfield's employees. But Garfield had always believed that physicians should be working for themselves. To make that happen, Sidney Garfield literally gave away his practice to the Permanente partners in Northern and Southern California. This unparalleled act of generosity enabled both Groups to form their partnerships, The Permanente Medical Group on February 21, 1948, the Southern California Permanente Medical Group on January 1, 1953.

Cecil Cutting, of The Permanente Medical Group, estimated that when Garfield gave away his Northern California practice, it was worth $1 million in 1948 dollars. Southern California was probably worth a bit less being, at the time, a newer and smaller Group. Garfield asked nothing and received nothing from the new partners for their shares in what had been up until then a solely-owned medical practice.[54] [Partners were required to put up money to "buy in" to the partnership, but the money went for the operating capital of the partnership, not to Garfield. The partnership agreement in Southern California called for a $5,000 investment from each partner;[55] $10,000 from each partner in Northern California.[56]]

Sidney Garfield would remain with the Kaiser Permanente organization until 1971, when he retired from the Board of Directors. He spent his remaining years writing numerous articles and books on health care, primarily on prepayment systems, health maintenance, health testing and health promotion. His later years brought national recognition and awards for his accomplishments. In 1969, the Group Health Association of America presented Dr. Garfield with its Distinguished Service Award. In October 1977, he received the Lyndon Baines Johnson Award for Humanitarian Service. Two years after his death, his alma mater, the University of Southern California, dedicated the Sidney R. Garfield Chair in the Health Sciences, made possible by a million-dollar grant from the Henry J. Kaiser Family Foundation. The Chair would be awarded to a medical scientist interested in preventive medicine and health policy studies.

At his death, Sidney Garfield's lifelong friend, Dr. Cecil Cutting, remarked that, "He captured the principles and significance of prepayment to a group of physicians as a more efficient and effective mechanism for health care. He developed the concept against opposition and obstructions that would have been overwhelming to many without his dedication and courage."[57] Said James A. Vohs, then Chairman and President of Kaiser Foundation Health Plan and Kaiser Foundation Hospitals, "Dr. Garfield's contributions to our Program and to medical care in the United States are beyond measure. All of us associated with Kaiser Permanente are indebted to him for his vision, for his leadership, and for his untiring commitment to our Program."[58]

LOOKING AHEAD

During the 1980s, the Southern California Permanente Medical Group changed dramatically because the health care environment had changed dramatically. Now there was stiff competition. The government was regulating the cost and scope of services. SCPMG responded to these changes by changing itself. It took on a more business-like orientation to control costs. It developed a new regional structure that allowed for better allocation of resources and it steadied its relationship with the Health Plan so the two entities could face outside pressures with a united front.

The 1990s would bring yet another set of challenges, among them even more competition and considerable employer and governmental unhappiness about the skyrocketing cost of health care. SCPMG's next decade would be just as tough as its last.

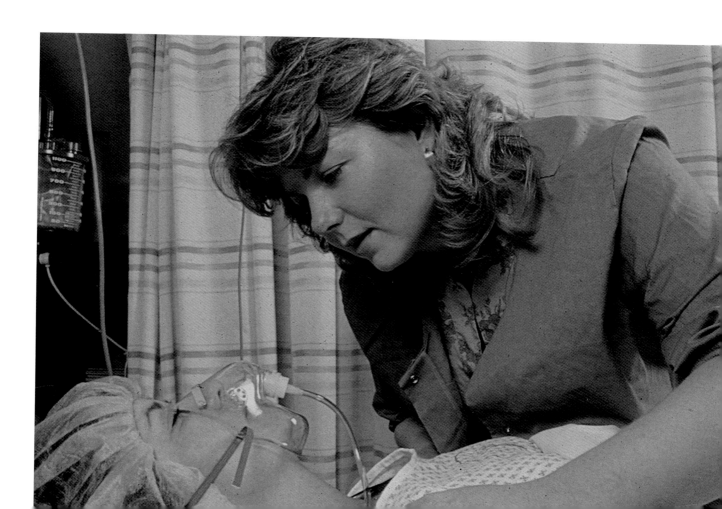

CHAPTER SEVEN

THE 1990s/2000s . . .
TRIUMPHING OVER ADVERSITY

"I never had any doubts that in spite
of all the opposition we met, that we
would end up succeeding."

— *Irv Klitsner, MD*

LEFT
*Baldwin Park Medical Center under
construction*

RIGHT
*Metro Service Area Leadership Team
Janet Rees, Joseph Hummel, Fred Lapsys,
MD, Ivette Estrada, Fred Alexander, MD,
Pat Crowe*

BACKGROUND
*Baldwin Park Medical Center
construction site*

TRANSFORMATION

DURING the 1990s, SCPMG and Kaiser Permanente would face several major crises serious enough to threaten the future of the medical care program. Vigorous competitors who promised better service and care were taking a serious bite out of membership in Southern California. From the Kaiser Permanente Program Office came news that some Southern California hospitals were going to be closed. And, in a particularly demoralizing development, the Health Plan announced its decision to merge the Southern and Northern California Regions into a single "Division".

Through it all, SCPMG would initiate an unprecedented effort to improve service and quality of care. The Medical Group would also launch many special programs to enhance the care of its culturally diverse population, of women, the elderly and patients with disabilities, to mention only a few. These efforts were instrumental in establishing SCPMG as a first-rate provider; certainly a key factor in building Southern California membership from about 2.2 million people in 1990 to 3.1 million by 2003.

NEW LEADERSHIP FOR THE 90S

In the early 1990s, Dr. Frank Murray, who had guided SCPMG through the difficult 1980s, announced that he would retire in December 1993. In November 1992, SCPMG elected Dr. Oliver Goldsmith as its next Medical Director, his term to begin in January 1994. In the meantime, he would work side-by-side with Dr. Murray to become familiar with the duties and responsibilities of his new position.

Oliver Goldsmith had received his medical degree from UCLA, completed his internship at the Wadsworth Veterans Hospital in Los Angeles and his residency training at UCLA Medical Center. While at Wadsworth, Goldsmith had met Dr. Harold Frankl, an attending gastroenterologist at the Veterans Hospital and Chief of Gastroenterology at the Los Angeles Medical Center. In 1969, Hal Frankl invited Oliver Goldsmith to visit his department and meet some physicians. Goldsmith was impressed. "I liked the physicians I met and identified with what they were doing and their style of practice."[1]

Hal Frankl also liked what he saw in Oliver Goldsmith. "I was incredibly enthusiastic that we found a wonderful candidate and I just hoped and prayed that we could entice him to actually be a member of the department," recalled Frankl. "He was young and enthusiastic. I knew that he'd come from a first-class training program and he just hit all the right buttons. He had the attitudes that were necessary. He had the education. He was obviously very bright. He was just what any department would love to have."[2]

Goldsmith's last step in the interview process was a meeting with Ray Kay who quickly assessed the new candidate. "Ray Kay wrote 'nice boy' on my file," noted Goldsmith with a smile when interviewed in 2003.[3] Kay invited Goldsmith to join the Medical Group.

Oliver Goldsmith began his career with SCPMG as a staff physician in the Gastroenterology Department at the LA Medical Center. "From day one," said Hal Frankl, "it was obvious he was really good. Patients loved him. He was knowledgeable. He was direct. He fit in perfectly." But it was also obvious to Frankl that, in addition to clinical practice, Goldsmith was looking for other opportunities in the Medical Group. "He'd gone very early on to the Medical Director at Sunset to look for area-wide tasks that he could help in," said Frankl. "So although he did a marvelous job in the department, he already had his eye on the bigger subject."[4]

Goldsmith quickly moved up the Medical Group's administrative ranks, starting in 1973 when he was elected to the SCPMG Board of Directors. He would go on to serve in many important capacities, including Chief of Internal Medicine at the West Los Angeles Medical Center from 1979 to 1988 and Area Associate Medical Director at West LA from 1989 to 1993, when he became SCPMG's Medical Director-elect.

OLIVER GOLDSMITH, MD

A *Young Oliver (lower left) with family, 1942*
B *Oliver Goldsmith age 5*
C *Age 17*
E *In the Army Reserves 1960s*
F *2003*
G *1961*
H WITH *President Clinton during a press conference on the medically uninsured, 1997*
J *Meeting with Surgeon General David Satcher, MD*

CREATING MEMBER SERVICE AREAS

In 1988, Frank Murray, then SCPMG Medical Director, and Hugh Jones, Regional Manager for Health Plan, had begun looking ahead to the challenges they believed the Southern California Region would face in the 1990s and beyond — key among them, its centralized management.

Murray and Jones believed that the highly centralized management structure that had developed was negatively affecting operations, and above all, member service. "I looked at the organizational design and I felt that most all decisions were being made centrally," said Murray. "I wasn't entirely convinced that tight central control was the way to get the best outcome for our Health Plan members." Murray and Jones assembled a Strategic Action Team to rethink the organizational design. Murray had a plan. "I felt there was a need to find an effective way to decentralize the authority and increase the accountability and responsibility in the service areas."[5]

After Oliver Goldsmith became Medical Director-elect, Murray involved him in the efforts to decentralize. Goldsmith agreed that decentralization was a good idea and that the centralized bureaucracy had made it extremely difficult to initiate changes on the local level. As Goldsmith explained in 1994, "Any one of us who has tried to carry an idea through the organization, whether successful or not, says to themselves, 'I can't go through this again.' [. . .] All of us asked the question, 'Was this process adding value for our members?'"[6] Clearly, Medical Group leaders did not think it was.

In 1994, SCPMG and the Health Plan endorsed the idea of creating Member Service Areas. It would be an all-out effort, noted Goldsmith, "to make Walnut Center's [Regional headquarters] head smaller and the body bigger."

The plan to decentralize called for the creation of six geographic subregions, or Member Service Areas. Some of these service areas would include just one medical center, some would have two, and some would have three. The new MSAs were San Diego; Orange County; Inland Empire (Riverside and Fontana); Tri Central (Harbor City, Bellflower and Baldwin Park); Metro

Valley

Metro Los Angeles

Tri Central

Inland Empire

Orange County

San Die

(West Los Angeles and Los Angeles); and the Valley (Woodland Hills, Panorama City and Bakersfield).

Goldsmith described the new structure as having "great importance for us and our members. [. . .] The aim is a transformation from a 'command control' model to that of self-managed, accountable, responsible decision-making units. [. . .] The key is to be responsible for what you are accountable for. In this new arrangement, a host of matters are best resolved at the MSA level."[7]

Just as Goldsmith wanted to explain what subregionalization was, he also wanted to explain what it was not. "Clearly, this is not a form of dismemberment. We are one organization in Southern California. Much of our strength is attributable to our large market share. What we are promoting is an arrangement of the parts that brings us closer to our members and at the same time maintains our advantages of size. [. . .] If anything, this strengthens physician management where it should be most strong — where the members are."[8]

According to Goldsmith, the idea was that each Member Service Area knew its members best, and could serve them best, "if given the opportunity to develop the personality of the local subregion."

The Health Plan had initially proposed that one medical director be appointed for each Member Service Area, regardless of how many medical centers were involved. "For instance in the Inland Empire," said Goldsmith, "Health Plan proposed having one medical director run both Riverside and Fontana. I said no. The personality of each medical center requires its own leadership."

While the medical centers in each Member Service Area retained their own leadership and autonomy, they were expected to work together as partners. "The advantages of partnership versus assimilation are that you get the culture of compromise, the wisdom of both sides, the retention of the culture and the uniqueness of each area and you get a more highly-performing organization with more communication," said Goldsmith.

Ideally, this partnership would result in the sharing of personnel, plans and resources. "For example," said Goldsmith, "Panorama City used to hire its own specialists and Woodland Hills would hire its own specialists, but often there wasn't enough for the specialist to do at one medical center, so we had them do general things. Now we can hire one specialist to cover both medical centers. So the surgeon is happy because he or she gets to do their specialty all day long; and the two centers get the benefit. That's an example of partnering. Partnering is sharing."

There had been talk at one time about making each MSA into a separate Permanente Medical Group, in a sense destroying the larger SCPMG and creating six separate Permanente Medical Groups in Southern California. In the mid-1950s, during the troubled years leading up to the Tahoe Conference, Henry Kaiser had also suggested creating separate medical groups within a Region. At the time, Kaiser's move was seen as a divide-and-conquer tactic, and many viewed the current proposal in the same light. Now, as then, the idea of separation was rejected. The whole point of subregionalization was not to create separate groups, but to retain the power of a large single Medical Group while achieving more local autonomy.

The benefits of forming Member Service Areas soon became apparent. By 1996, Oliver Goldsmith noted, "I am beginning to see specific departments getting together for their education, sharing consultants, developing similar objectives and even working at one another's Medical Center [. . .] in order to support clinical quality in the MSA."[9] In 2001, in speaking about the MSAs, Goldsmith noted, "I think most of you would agree this was the right thing to do. Over the last eight years, it has changed our culture. It allowed us to coordinate Call Centers and many other services more logically. It has also allowed us to build upon our core strength — effective partnering."[10]

THREAT OF HOSPITAL CLOSURES

In the mid-1990s, just as SCPMG was setting up the new Member Service Areas, the Medical Group was faced with the disheartening news that some of its hospitals were going to be closed.

The decision had been made jointly by Medical Group and Health Plan leadership. It was a tough decision but, at the time, it seemed the only alternative. Membership was down, hospital utilization was continuing to decrease both inside and outside Kaiser Permanente, hospital beds were going empty and the cost of running the hospitals continued to rise. Then there was the issue of seismic safety. California legislation passed following the 1994 Northridge earthquake required all hospitals to meet tough new seismic standards. The older hospitals in the Southern California Region — Los Angeles, Fontana, Harbor City, Panorama City and Bellflower — would require major renovation or rebuilding in order to comply.

Together, SCPMG and Health Plan leadership decided not to rebuild, but to close the older facilities and begin using community hospitals. Virtually no one in the Medical Group liked the idea, least of all Oliver Goldsmith. He, like most, believed that Kaiser Permanente's unique character and quality of care grew, in part, from treating its own members in its own hospitals. Now, that time-honored tradition was being abandoned.

Yet, as much as Goldsmith disliked the idea of closing hospitals, it seemed the right thing to do. As Medical Director he was determined to lead the effort "to execute this major change skillfully" — like it or not. Goldsmith would call the decision to start closing

hospitals one of the most difficult and challenging of his tenure. "When I originally embraced the idea of closing Kaiser Hospitals and practicing in community hospitals I can assure everyone it was based on sound thinking and looking at the enormous capital structure of our program and our competition."

Closures were to begin with Kaiser Permanente Los Angeles Medical Center (Sunset), the oldest hospital in the Southern California system.

The painful process started on November 21, 1996 when the Southern California Region signed a letter of intent to discuss shifting acute-care patients from the Los Angeles Medical Center to the 380-bed St. Vincent Medical Center, less than 3 miles away near downtown Los Angeles. St. Vincent was owned by Catholic Healthcare West (CHW), a 35-hospital system based in San Francisco. CHW and Kaiser Permanente were the state's two largest hospital systems. Sharing hospital facilities seemed a good idea for both organizations.

Under the plan, all Kaiser Permanente members who would normally have been hospitalized at LAMC would now go to St. Vincent's, where they would be seen by their Permanente physician. Other than that, members would see little difference. They would continue to go to existing Kaiser Permanente facilities to see both their primary care and specialty physicians, to pick up their prescriptions, for eye exams and for lab work — everything but hospitalization.

The LAMC hospital was slated for closure in mid-1997. Kaiser Permanente was also thinking about having Catholic Healthcare West manage the hospital at the Baldwin Park Medical Center. (The Baldwin Park hospital floors had been completed in 1994, but never opened.) The hospitals in Harbor City, Panorama City, Bellflower and Fontana were next on the closure list. Oliver Goldsmith tried to prepare the Area Associate Medical Directors for the distinct possibility that some of their hospitals would be closed. "I would say to the medical directors there," recalled Goldsmith, "if I appoint you to this job, you might have to carry out closing your own hospital. Are you prepared to do that? Don't even take the job if you're going to fight me because I make the decision."

Fortunately, he would not have to. After the initial letter of intent was signed in 1996, studies indicated that St. Vincent's did not have the capacity to handle member needs. And, in a case of perfect timing, membership was starting to rise. The proposed consolidation was off. Kaiser Permanente would keep its hospitals open and run them as solely-owned and operated Kaiser Permanente facilities.

SCPMG breathed a collective sigh of relief. Soon plans were announced to renovate or replace hospitals in Los Angeles, Bellflower, Fontana, Harbor City, Panorama City, West Los Angeles and Anaheim. "It's a lot more fun to plan rebuilding hospitals than work on closing them," Goldsmith told the Board in 2000.

CRISIS WITH THE HEALTH PLAN

While the hospital closure issue was still on the table, SCPMG faced a major crisis with the Health Plan. The problem began in 1996 when the Health Plan unilaterally decided to consolidate all its operations statewide into a single California Division. If executed, the plan would effectively end the separate Southern and Northern California Regions that had existed since the 1940s. By now, Kaiser Permanente was a national program with other Permanente Medical Groups and Regions around the country. They too would be consolidated into Divisions.

There were a number of reasons stated for the planned consolidation. Among them, it would save money to consolidate administrative, marketing and support functions. Consolidation would make it easier for major statewide employers to deal with a single source in California rather than two relatively autonomous units, one in the South and one in the North. The consolidation, said the Health Plan, would also help them create an integrated national organization.

SCPMG and the other Permanente Medical Groups could understand the Health Plan's need to centralize a number of activities. "We are supporting this, the leveraging advantages in IT, purchasing, marketing, etc.," Goldsmith told the Board early in 1998. "These can be wise moves in the competitive health care world." But what the Medical Group couldn't understand was the way the Health Plan was going about the consolidation, unilaterally and without consensus. The implications were disturbing. "These unilateral changes and lack of consensus building and

1998

Baldwin Park opens as full-fledged Medical Center (The medical center opened in stages, starting in 1991 with the opening of its first medical office building. The hospital building was completed in 1994 and, while the medical offices opened, the hospital floors remained closed. Hospital floors opened in October 1998.)

2002

California Division dissolved; Southern California Region reestablished

2003

SCPMG celebrates its 50th anniversary

2004

Jeffrey Weisz becomes SCPMG's sixth Medical Director

mutuality strongly implied a new and less balanced relationship with the Permanente Medical Groups," said Goldsmith. "For someone like me, steeped in the culture and values of Kaiser Permanente, this was truly a surprise and disappointment." Goldsmith, in fact, believed that unilateral decisions by either the Medical Groups or Health Plan undermined the program. "Speaking personally," said Goldsmith, "I deeply believe a consensus mode within Kaiser Permanente is best; without it, I believe there is true peril ahead."[11] Prophetic words.

Richard Cordova, President, Kaiser Foundation Health Plan / Hospitals, Southern California Region and Oliver Goldsmith, MD, Medical Director / Chairman of the Board, SCPMG

In March 1996, the Health Plan held a meeting to announce their decision to consolidate. The Permanente Medical Groups unanimously decided not to attend, not so much to protest the consolidation, but the fact that the decision had been made without consensus.

The Health Plan merged California operations in January 1997. In speaking to the Board early in 1997, Oliver Goldsmith clearly expressed his disappointment: "Well, Mr. Barnaby [President and Chief Operating Officer of Kaiser Foundation Health Plan and Hospitals] and David Lawrence [Chairman and CEO of Kaiser Foundation Health Plan and Hospitals] have ended Kaiser Health Plan Regions in Northern and Southern California. They have departed from the consensus

decision-making process that guided us for so many years." On the heels of the consolidation announcement came another announcement, that Hugh Jones (Health Plan manager in the Southern California Region) and David Pockell (Jones's counterpart in Northern California) would be leaving the organization.

Traditionally, there had always been a Health Plan leader (most recently, Hugh Jones) in Southern California to work with the SCPMG Medical Director, sharing leadership for the program. Under the new Division arrangement, the position of Regional Health Plan Manager was eliminated. "I had no Health Plan partner in Southern California," said Goldsmith. "There was no one in the Region for me to talk to. Every time I wanted to talk to someone in the Health Plan, I had to fly up to Oakland."

Instead of helping the organization, the new Division structure had just the opposite effect. Kaiser Permanente took a financial nosedive, losing a half billion dollars in 1997, another half billion in 1998. Why? As Goldsmith explained, "Because California lost its focus and forgot how to do business. Because they [Health Plan] ruined the partnership. The partnership is Health Plan and Medical Group in the Region, working on performance. We had such a strained relationship that our financial performance began to deteriorate." The downward financial spiral would continue into 1999. "They wrote our obituary," said Dr. Les Zendle, Associate Medical Director of Clinical Services, 1993–2003. "People both inside and outside the organization thought Kaiser Permanente wouldn't make it."[12]

But just as the Medical Group would criticize Health Plan leadership for the debacle, it would also credit them with trying to salvage the situation. The turnaround would occur step by step, starting with the appointment of Richard Pettingill as California Division President as of January 1, 1999. Pettingill replaced Richard Barnaby, who had been serving as California Division President on an interim basis. Barnaby announced that he planned to retire at the end of 1999.

Goldsmith believed that Pettingill's appointment was a good choice and a good sign. "I welcome Dick Pettingill, who more clearly appreciates the importance of the Medical Group," said Goldsmith. "He and I recognize that while together we can leverage back-office functions, operations need to be focused on Southern and Northern California."[13] Although the Division structure remained intact, one of Pettingill's first moves was to restore Health Plan leadership in Southern California with the appointment of Richard Cordova as the Chief Operating Officer (COO) for Southern California. Mary Ann Thode was named COO for Northern California.

The new leadership, and the renewed spirit of partnership it represented, helped repair the strained relationship between SCPMG and the Health Plan. "Both sides have made considerable progress in developing interpersonal trust," said Goldsmith, speaking in 1999. "They have begun to reconstitute some of the analytic and program functions that had been neglected in the South. I think both sides recognize that a unified team in Southern California will be a powerful support to performance. That explains Mr. Cordova's appointment."[14]

The relationship between SCPMG (and the other medical groups) and Health Plan would continue to improve and, with it, financial performance. The Division structure, which had proved so divisive, was mostly on its way out.

In July 2001, David Lawrence, who had been instrumental in creating the Divisions, announced that he would be retiring in December 2002. In March 2002, Kaiser Permanente named George Halvorson, then president and CEO of HealthPartners, a leading nonprofit, integrated health care organization in Minneapolis, Minnesota, to replace Lawrence. Within weeks of taking office, Halvorson announced the end of the Division structure and returned California to its two original Regions. In August 2002, Richard Cordova was named president of the Kaiser Foundation Health Plan and Hospitals (KFHP/H) in Southern California; Mary Ann Thode, president of KFHP/H in Northern California.

In looking back, Goldsmith said: "The Division structure was well-intended. It tried to unify back-office functions and present a common face to California. But it simply did not fit our operations."[15]

What did fit was the Regional structure. "What should not be overlooked within Kaiser Permanente in the quest for benchmark performance is the regional linkage between the insurance and health care delivery functions," said Goldsmith. "This linkage was a stroke of genius. It has provided 50 years of alignment in the service of our members. I hope no one forgets this. I know it is all about achieving a sustainable competitive advantage. Our integrated and aligned approach has done that for 50 years."[16]

Although the attempted consolidation had been disastrous, it did generate some positive outcomes. The restored partnership between SCPMG and the Health Plan would be better than ever. "The Medical Group's relationship with the Health Plan today is the best it's been for 20 or 30 years," said Goldsmith in 2003. He attributed a good share of that success to his Health Plan partner, Richard Cordova. "Mr. Cordova is in the mold of a true partner. He believes in partnering with the Medical Group. We trust each other."

The crisis also strengthened the bond among the historically autonomous Permanente Medical Groups. The Medical Groups had always had a kind of informal relationship and their leaders would meet on occasion, but there had been no formal organization uniting the Medical Groups nationally. But now the Medical Groups felt it necessary to have such an organization to strengthen their position with the Health Plan and form a more equitable partnership. On January 6, 1997, all the Medical Groups nationwide joined forces to create The Permanente Federation. The newly formed Federation appointed Dr. Francis J. Crosson from The Permanente Medical Group in Northern California as Executive Director. Dr. Goldsmith became one of the first four members of the Federation's Executive Committee.

The Permanente Federation would not only help the Permanente Medical Groups create a more effective partnership with the Health Plan, it would also encourage more cooperation among the Groups. Today, SCPMG physicians often travel to other Medical Groups, sharing successful practices and providing administrative (and sometimes clinical) support.

Patient care at Kaiser Permanente is a team effort, with physicians and nurses working together as partners. "SCPMG provides the opportunity for nurses to experience a true partnership and collaborative relationship with the physicians," said Terry Bream, RN, MN, Manager, Department of Clinical Services. "Kaiser Permanente is not as hierarchical and tradition-bound as other healthcare organizations. The physicians in this Medical Group are very aware that medicine isn't practiced with only one profession, but instead is practiced as a team effort where everyone is respected for the unique and essential skills they bring to the table. Nurses are treated as colleagues and widely acknowledged for their contributions."

Nurses working with SCPMG are encouraged to pursue professional growth. "The Medical Group provides so many choices in terms of taking a nursing career and building on those skills," said Bream. "Whether it's working in critical care and then choosing to go back to our CRNA program; whether it's taking a basic nursing degree and going back to earn an advanced degree, then entering management or entering a clinical specialty; whether it's starting in a record room and becoming a medical assistant and then getting financial support to go back to nursing school, the options and opportunities are endless."

The doors are also open at SCPMG for nurses to follow more unconventional career paths. As Terry Bream explains, "The organization is so open and creative in terms of how it takes a person with a clinical background and then puts him or her into a whole other avenue of skill sets. For example, I had a traditional job as an in-patient nurse administrator for the Los Angeles Medical Center, but have since made the transition from that traditional nursing role into one of an administrator working with the Medical Group. And I'm only one example of how someone educated in one profession can grow and be recognized for many other skills. So there's a great opportunity here for everyone to participate and contribute to the administration of this partnership. I feel that I have a very strong professional voice in decisions that affect Kaiser Permanente and the healthcare of California and perhaps the healthcare of the nation. These opportunities don't exist in a local community hospital or an academic setting."

All the opportunities that Kaiser Permanente provides continue to be a major factor in its ability to attract and retain nurses at a time when the nation is experiencing a nursing shortage. "The country has such a void of young men and women who want to become nurses, that you do want to be the employer of choice," said Bream. "It's nice to know that healthcare providers are not only choosing Kaiser Permanente but are also staying and not going elsewhere because this is the best place to practice."

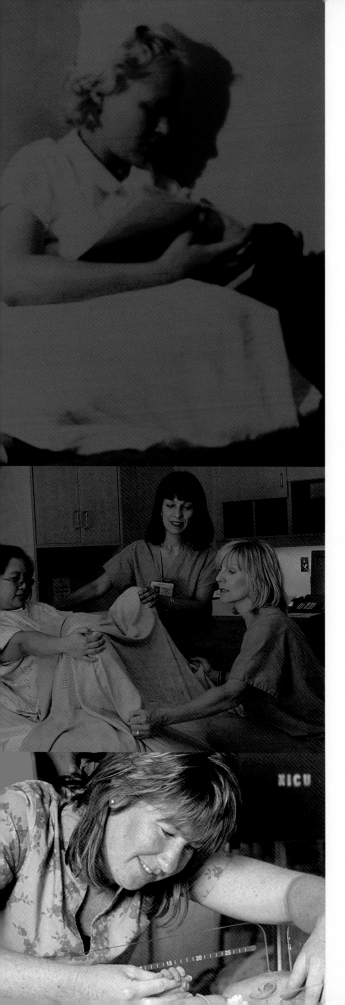

In the early 1990s, the Los Angeles Medical Center Department of Nursing crafted this philosophy to reflect its heartfelt belief that nursing at Kaiser Permanente offers limitless possibilities and far exceeds its traditional boundaries.

— *Terry Bream, RN, MN*

THIS IS NURSING

ADVOCATE

- I speak for the patient when another voice is needed
- I stand up for patient's right

EXPERT

- I care for the patient with special knowledge and skill
- I apply my clinical experience in a complex environment

PROFESSIONAL

- I bring to the patient's bedside the best possible education
- I take pride in my learned profession

COLLEAGUE

- I collaborate with the physician and other members of the health care team
- I respect and am respected by my colleagues

CAREERIST

- I value the traditions and history of nursing
- I promote a positive professional image

LEADER

- I take charge of the patient's plan of care to promote the best results
- I create and inspire vision for nursing's future

FOCUSING ON QUALITY

For three years — 1992, 1993 and 1994 — membership in Southern California had been in a serious decline. In 1994, for example, the Region suffered a net loss of 30,000 members. The losses were due in part to a sluggish economy in Southern California following the end of the Cold War. Local defense contractors such as McDonnell Douglas and Lockheed cut back operations and laid off huge numbers of employees, many of whom were Kaiser Permanente members.

Competition from other HMOs was also a major factor in the membership decline of the early 90s. The presence of many competitors now gave purchasers and consumers a real choice in the marketplace and some, who might have joined Kaiser Permanente in the past, were now going elsewhere. Why? First, Kaiser Permanente lost some of its price advantage as competitor HMOs leveraged payment cuts to physicians and hospitals and learned how to become more efficient — like Kaiser Permanente. Second, some people believed that other health plans offered better care and more personalized service than Kaiser Permanente. Without a price advantage, issues of quality and service became more important to the purchasers and consumers of health care.

For the first time, large purchasers like Pacific Bell and CalPERS (the state and local government purchaser of health benefits) wanted data about Kaiser Permanente's quality. "Kaiser Permanente had to demonstrate to employer groups and patients that we could deliver high quality and service," said Les Zendle. "We had to prove it to the purchasers because they decide which plans to offer their employees, and we had to prove it to their employees so they would select and stay with Kaiser Permanente. Purchasers used to ask us, 'How much do you cost?' All of a sudden we started to get additional questions like, 'How do you measure quality?' and 'How do we know you're measuring it?' and 'How do we know you're taking action based on what you find?'"[17]

The primary responsibility for measuring and improving both quality and service fell to SCPMG's Department of Clinical Services. The Department had been headed by Sam Sapin since 1982. Upon Dr. Sapin's retirement from SCPMG in 1989, Dr. Richard Rodriguez became the Associate Medical Director for Clinical Services. In 1992, Rodriguez was selected to be the Medical Director of the Southeast (Georgia) Permanente Medical Group. Les Zendle was chosen by Frank Murray and the newly-elected SCPMG Medical Director Oliver Goldsmith to replace Rodriguez.

Dr. Les Zendle had joined SCPMG in 1980 as an internist at the Harbor City Medical Center. He became interested in geriatric medicine in the early 1980s, taking on various roles at Harbor City. In 1986 Frank Murray asked him to help the Region deal with its increasing population of older members. In addition to promoting the use of nurse practitioners to help physicians manage patients in nursing homes, Les Zendle helped develop the Geriatric "Model of Care" — which in the 1990s would become the prototype for a "population care management" approach to patients with chronic diseases or conditions. Two years after becoming Associate Medical Director of Clinical Services, Dr. Zendle chose Terry Bream, the nursing executive at the Los Angeles Medical Center, as the manager of the department.

Although there had been formal efforts to demonstrate and improve quality and service in the 1970s and 1980s, they had been internally focused — one Kaiser Permanente Region or department comparing itself against another Kaiser Permanente Region or department. Now, purchasers in the 1990s wanted to compare Kaiser Permanente to other health plans. Purchasers wanted 'report cards' that they could share with their employees. Organizations like the Pacific Business Group on Health wanted to publicly report these results.

But what performance measures should be compared? At the time, none had been established, so in 1990, Kaiser Permanente, along with representatives from the Permanente Medical Groups, began working with other plans, providers and major purchasers (under the auspices of the newly-created National Committee for Quality Assurance — NCQA) to develop a set of performance standards and measures. The clinical and service measures, which included items such as childhood immunization, breast and cervical cancer screening rates, as well as member surveys of service satisfaction, became part of NCQA's Healthplan Employer Data and Information Set (HEDIS).

Purchasers also expected Kaiser Permanente, along with other health plans, to undergo NCQA accreditation — another validation that health plans met certain standards and practices to assure the delivery of high quality care and service. Kaiser Permanente Southern California underwent its first NCQA accreditation in 1995, achieving the highest accreditation available at the time. The Southern California Region has continued to earn NCQA accreditation, and currently holds "Excellent" NCQA status, the highest accreditation mark that can be awarded.

The challenge, however, was not just to collect data and meet accreditation standards; it was to improve clinical performance. SCPMG's desire to improve performance would lead to many efforts in the 1990s. Key among them were the development of Clinical Strategic Goals, the development and use of clinical practice guidelines and the promotion of Population Care Management. "The organizational focus on annual Clinical Strategic Goals helped channel our energy and resources towards a vital few priority areas," said Zendle. "It also made it easier to get the attention and commitment of physicians and staff to improve these results." Dr. Joel Hyatt, an Assistant to the Associate Medical Director of Clinical Services since 1989, led this effort beginning in 1993. Dr. John Brookey took over this responsibility in 1998 when he became chairperson of the Region's Quality Committee.

To further improve clinical effectiveness and efficiency, SCPMG began developing evidence-based clinical practice guidelines in 1992. Clinical practice guidelines (CPGs) are recommendations based on medical evidence, as well as expert opinion, on how best to care for most patients with a specific disease or medical condition. Dr. Allen Bredt, then Chief of Internal Medicine at the Panorama City Medical Center

The purpose of SCPMG's Department of Clinical Services is to provide leadership, consultation and support for SCPMG's physicians, administrators and staff in order to improve the delivery of medical services and to demonstrate the clinical value of Permanente Medicine to Kaiser Permanente members and the community.

— *Les Zendle, MD, Associate Medical Director Clinical Services, 1993–2003*

Sam Sapin, MD and Les Zendle, MD at the dedication of the new Center for Medical Education at the Los Angeles Medical Center, July 2001

and later an Assistant to the Associate Medical Director of Clinical Services, led SCPMG's effort to develop and implement CPGs. Bredt partnered with David Eddy, a nationally renowned expert in conceptualizing how to assess scientific evidence and use those assessments to determine the best ways to render care. Dr. Eddy became a Senior Advisor to both the SCPMG Medical Director and the Kaiser Foundation Health Plan/Hospitals Regional Manager (now called President). SCPMG's clinical practice guideline development processes have been recognized for their thoroughness, active participation of SCPMG clinical experts, and solid methodologies. According to Les Zendle, "Clinical practice guidelines help physicians know what the medical literature and clinical experts say are the most effective tests or treatments for a population of patients with a specific disease or condition. The physician then takes into consideration the unique aspects of the individual patient to determine what to recommend for that particular patient."

Joel Hyatt also led SCPMG's effort in Population Care Management. Population Care Management looks at patients with a specific disease or condition, identifies those at greatest risk for complications, and develops systems and processes to help physicians make sure that

these patients get the tests and treatments known to lead to better outcomes. SCPMG's efforts preceded and linked up nicely with the Care Management Institute, a national Kaiser Permanente program formed in 1997.

Hand-in-hand with the effort to improve clinical quality, was the effort to improve service to Kaiser Permanente members. "People started thinking about service as a business issue," said Adrienne Cotterell, Director of Quality Assessment and Improvement from January 1988 to August 2000.[18] SCPMG increased the use of several kinds of member satisfaction surveys — to survey current members, members who had terminated membership in the Health Plan, and members of other health plans to learn how they felt about their own plan and how they perceived Kaiser Permanente. These surveys were especially valuable in identifying specific areas to improve service, such as appointment and telephone access, as well as patient perceptions of their relationships with their doctors.

In the early 1990s, SCPMG began using a survey called MAPPS (Member Appraisal of Physician and Provider Services), a variation of a survey tool developed in Kaiser Permanente's Colorado Region. "MAPPS is very important because we knew from our own data that the biggest predictor of overall member satisfaction

with the Health Plan is a patient's relationship with his or her doctor," said Oliver Goldsmith. "In other words, patients who perceive that their physicians care about them, listen and communicate well are more likely to be satisfied with Kaiser Permanente's care and remain members."

The idea of patients rating their physicians was new and many physicians were skeptical about the idea. "Physicians believed that their technical expertise defined clinical quality, but many were unaware that patients often judge clinical quality through the quality of the doctor-patient relationship," said Les Zendle. MAPPS was rolled out region-wide in 1994. In addition, training programs were developed to help physicians improve how they communicate with patients.

The agendas of the Chiefs of Service groups, created by Sam Sapin in the early 1980s to promote cooperation between medical centers, evolved over 20 years to focus on improving quality and service. Dr. Jo Carol Hiatt, an Assistant to the Associate Medical Director of Clinical Services, whose main responsibility was liaison to the Chiefs of Service groups, stated "now discussions on clinical strategic goals, population care management, clinical practice guidelines and service metrics occur at almost every meeting."

The focus on improving service began to have an effect. Noted Oliver Goldsmith in 1996, "There can be no question that our Kaiser Health Plan members have recognized that something has changed inside of Kaiser Permanente. [. . .] Purchaser representatives have said to me, 'Our members notice the difference in response time on the phones and the friendliness of the staff. One patient said to me, "When the phone [was] answered so quickly and someone said, 'When would you like the appointment,' I thought I must have the wrong number — this isn't Kaiser Permanente."' There is also a lot of hard information that this improvement has been recognized by our members. The Pacific Business Group on Health gave us an 'A' for our Health Plan services as well as for our SCPMG physician quality."[19]

As public awareness of improved service rose, so did membership. After several years of declining numbers, 1996 would see a net growth of 190,000 members in Southern California. Fewer people dropped out. "I don't think anyone questions we are retaining members like never before," said Goldsmith in 1997.[20]

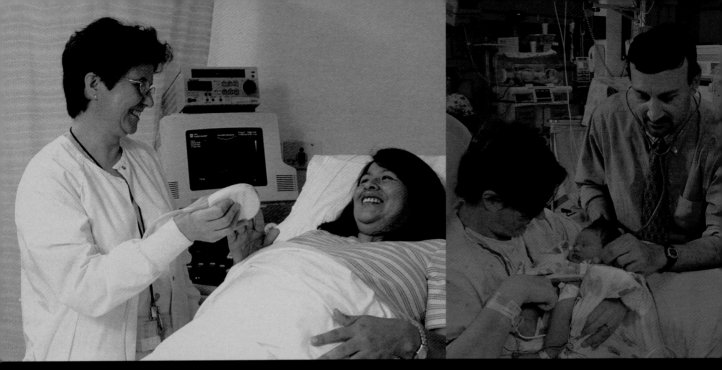

LEFT TO RIGHT: *Complicated Obstetrics, NICU, Pediatric Surgery, Pediatric Urology*

EVOLUTION OF THE RESEARCH AND EVALUATION PROGRAM

SCPMG physicians have long had the opportunity to conduct medical research. "Our research efforts really started in the late 1950s, spearheaded by Dr. Jack Cooper, who was the Chief of Urology at the Los Angeles Medical Center," recalled Dr. Sam Sapin. "Dr. Cooper was interested in looking for markers to detect prostate cancer. His efforts were funded internally, from the community service part of the budget, based on the fact that research was considered a benefit to the community. Other physicians from the Group who wanted to do research were also able to apply for internal funding. We had a committee that met once a year to look at these requests and we usually approved about 10 to 30 projects each year. That was how it worked until 1972, when I was appointed the Regional Director of Education and Research. At that time, I felt we needed to formalize the process, expand it and make it as user-friendly as possible to encourage physicians to do more research, feeling that this would benefit our physicians who were interested in research."[21]

As part of expanding its research efforts in the late 1970s, SCPMG created an Institution Review Board (IRB), required by the federal government for every institution conducting research on human subjects. "Following the establishment of our IRB," said Sapin, "the number of projects grew each year and the budget expanded accordingly."

In 1982, SCPMG's education and research functions were folded into the newly-created Department of Clinical Services, headed by Dr. Sapin. Dr. Sheldon Wolf, a neurologist at the Los Angeles Medical Center, was appointed the Regional Coordinator of Research. In the 1980s, SCPMG's desire to expand its research efforts and attract and accept external funding led to the 1988 creation of a separate department of Research and Evaluation within the Department of Clinical Services.

During the early 1990s, SCPMG launched an intensive search for a physician/researcher with extensive experience in obtaining external funds to head the Research and Evaluation Department. The search led to Dr. Diana Petitti, who was hired in 1993. A graduate of the Harvard Medical School, Dr. Petitti had previously worked as an epidemiologist for the Centers for Disease Control and Prevention (CDC), for Kaiser Permanente's Division of Research in Northern California, and had been a tenured faculty member at the University of California.

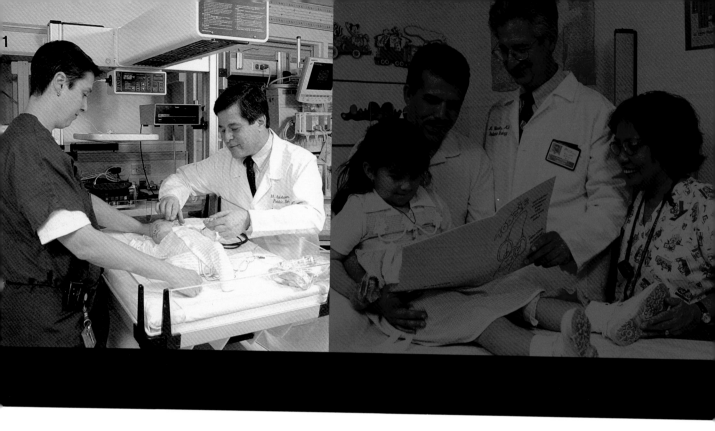

Under Dr. Petitti's leadership, the Department would create the administrative infrastructure necessary for SCPMG to expand its research program through outside funding. "Prior to the 1990s," said Dr. Petitti, "the amount of funds available internally for research was very limited and the organization did not really have the kind of infrastructure necessary to apply for outside funding. During the 1990s, our Department created the infrastructure that permits us to perform research using external funds. I can't emphasize enough the importance of this infrastructure in the growth of our research program. Today, about 80% of our research funds come from external sources."[22]

In addition to providing the infrastructure to facilitate research by the Medical Group, the Research and Evaluation Department also has added a cadre of full-time researchers to its staff. These researchers conduct about 20% of the research done in the Southern California Region, with SCPMG physicians often participating as consultants. For about 80% of the research projects, however, SCPMG physicians serve as principal investigators.

During the last decade, the number of research activities around the Southern California Region has grown significantly. In 1994, there were 290 active research projects, with 17 funded either by the federal government or a foundation. By 2001, the number of total projects had grown to 567, with 71 funded by federal or foundation sources. Dr. Petitti expects this rate of growth to continue. "We are still a relatively young research unit," she noted, "but we're very dynamic and we continue to seek opportunities to conduct projects that will advance medical knowledge."

WORKFORCE DIVERSITY AND CULTURALLY COMPETENT CARE

SCPMG had always taken steps to ensure equal employment opportunity, long before such policies were mandated by law. Dr. Ray Marcus recalled an incident in the 1950s that typified SCPMG's position even then. "We had a southern lady being X-rayed and a black technician was in the room with her," said Marcus. "She wrote this blistering letter to Ray Kay saying, 'How dare you have a black technician in the room with me.' Dr. Kay had his secretary write her back and say that at Kaiser that's how it is. We are all equal here. We are all American, and if you don't like it you can take some other plan but we're not changing."[23]

Over the years, SCPMG and the entire Kaiser Permanente organization had launched many efforts to promote and support workforce diversity. Since the late 1970s, Kaiser Permanente had been hosting a national diversity conference, where leaders in medicine, education and diversity training spoke of the importance of diversity in health care. In 1988, Kaiser Permanente created the National Diversity Council, a policy-making group to develop initiatives and goals related to workforce diversity. Oliver Goldsmith served for a time as the Council's chairman, giving SCPMG a national presence and voice on matters of diversity.

SCPMG promoted diversity in hiring physicians, nurses and staff, and encouraged women and minorities to enter management. The Medical Group worked to create a culture that valued diversity and respected the uniqueness of individuals. Physicians received Continuing Medical Education credits for taking diversity training. Starting in 1999, diversity training was included as part of all ongoing training programs for physicians, nurses, technicians and administrative staff. "We have tried very hard, and we're succeeding, not to end up a white-male-dominated Medical Group," said Oliver Goldsmith.

While achieving workforce diversity was an important goal in and of itself, Kaiser Permanente also believed that by having a diverse workforce it could better serve its highly diverse membership. Workforce diversity also helps create an environment to support the delivery of "culturally competent care."

Culturally competent care refers to health care that is sensitive to the beliefs and health status of different population groups. It acknowledges that different cultures have different needs and beliefs and that an understanding of those needs and beliefs can lead to better clinical outcomes. "Cultural competence does not require that patients be treated by using the same methods used in their country of origin," said Goldsmith. "However, cultural competency does create a compelling case for understanding the different ways patients act in a clinical setting and for communicating with patients to ensure the best possible clinical outcome."[24]

Promoting culturally competent care is encouraged and supported throughout the Region under the direction of Dr. Maria Carrasco, Regional Physician Coordinator of Culturally Responsive Care. Physicians receive help in understanding specific cultures through the use of Culturally Competent Care Handbooks published by the Kaiser Permanente National Diversity Council. There are a number of these handbooks, each focusing on a different population, including Latino; African American; Asian and Pacific Island American; and Lesbian, Gay, Bisexual and Transgendered. The handbooks explain, in great detail, how to better understand individual populations and the role that culture plays in treatment outcome.

To further its delivery of culturally competent care, SCPMG opened several clinical care modules that focus almost exclusively on specific populations. One module specifically for Asian American patients is located at the Montebello Medical Offices as a joint project between the Los Angeles and Baldwin Park Medical Centers. Another module to serve the Latino community is located in East Los Angeles, where eighty percent of the patient population is Latino. The East LA facility also serves as a Kaiser Permanente Center for Excellence, specializing in the treatment of diabetes, a prevalent disease among Latinos. In addition, the Center provides medical care for children who do not qualify for state funding due to immigration status, as part of the Kaiser Cares for Kids program. A module for African

Americans was established at the West Los Angeles Medical Center, where more than half the patient population is African American. This module focuses on the diagnosis, treatment and management of conditions especially prevalent among African Americans, including sickle cell disease, congestive heart failure and prostate cancer.

Every detail of these modules is designed to meet the needs of the community it serves. Signs are posted in the appropriate languages and physicians and staff members are bilingual where necessary. Physicians receive special training to diagnose and treat illnesses that may be uniquely associated with that community. Successful practices at these pilot locations will be integrated into future modules at additional sites.

CARING FOR PATIENTS WITH DISABILITIES

In July 2000, the Disability Rights Advocates, an Oakland-based nonprofit law center, filed suit against the Riverside and San Francisco Medical Centers, alleging that Kaiser Permanente had neglected the medical needs of people with disabilities. It was the first lawsuit of its kind in the country.

Part of the problem, said the lawsuit, was inaccessible medical equipment — examination tables that were too high or mammography equipment that could not be used by people in wheelchairs. The three plaintiffs in the suit all cited specific instances in which they had received inferior care due to the lack of appropriate equipment. One of the plaintiffs claimed to have had pressure sores on his buttocks for a year, but said that his doctor had not examined him because the exam table was inaccessible. Another plaintiff said she had not had a gynecological exam in more than fifteen years, also citing the lack of an exam table that could accommodate her wheelchair. Another patient claimed he had not been weighed for fifteen years because his doctor did not have a scale for patients in wheelchairs.

Dr. Michael Neri, Area Associate Medical Director in Riverside, discussed the problem with Dick Pettingill, then California Division President, and Kaiser Permanente counsel in Oakland. All agreed that the lawsuit was a serious charge that could result in considerable financial liability as well as negative publicity. Although the suit had singled out Riverside and San Francisco, many feared that similar suits would be filed against other medical centers throughout Southern and Northern California.

Rather than fight the suit, Neri and his colleagues decided to take another approach. "We began to look at how we could turn a potentially bad situation into something that would be very good for our organization," said Neri. "We decided to take the initiative and propose to the Disability Rights Advocates that we work with them in resolving their complaints."[25] The Kaiser Permanente team developed an approach to improve care for people with disabilities and presented

1998 SCPMG Board of Directors

FRONT ROW, L-R:

Kenneth Bell, MD, Associate Medical Director, Orange County; Michael Neri, MD, Associate Medical Director, Riverside; Faustina Navarez, MD, Obstetrics/Gynecology, Los Angeles; Les Zendle, MD, Associate Medical Director of Clinical Services; Oliver Goldsmith, MD, Medical Director; Irwin Goldstein, MD, Associate Medical Director/Physician Manager of Operations; Virginia Ambrozini, MD, Associate Medical Director, Panorama City; Maurice Alfaro, MD, Associate Medical Director, San Diego; Connie Iriarte, MD, Head and Neck Surgery, Bellflower; Thomas Godfrey, MD, Associate Medical Director, Los Angeles.

2ND ROW, L-R:

Marvin Ersher, MD, Family Practice, Baldwin Park; Peter Pellerito, Business Administrator; Harold Bass, MD, Pediatrics/Genetics, Panorama City; Melanie Hinson, MD, Internal Medicine, Harbor City; Albert Ray, MD, Family Practice, San Diego; M. Rudolph Brody, MD, Pediatrics, Los Angeles; Hansen Wang, MD, Surgery, Fontana; H.S. Kim, MD, Associate Medical Director, Bellflower.

3RD ROW, L-R:

Jonathan Siegel, MD, Internal Medicine, San Diego; Jeffrey Weisz, MD, Associate Medical Director, Woodland Hills; Edward Curry, MD, Pediatrics, Fontana; Kenneth Gould, MD, Internal Medicine/Infectious Disease, West Los Angeles; Donald Marcus, MD, Anesthesiology, Los Angeles; Jo Carol Hiatt, MD, Surgery, Panorama City; Gary Lulejian, MD, Associate Medical Director, Baldwin Park; David Lerman, MD, Secretary of the Board; O.W. Lim, MD, Obstetrics/Gynecology, Bellflower; Howard Levy, MD, Ophthalmology, Woodland Hills.

BACK ROW, L-R:

Douglas Killion, MD, Associate Medical Director, Harbor City; Philip Carney, Jr., MD, Associate Medical Director, Fontana; Gonzalo Garreton, MD, Obstetrics/Gynecology, Harbor City; William Geckeler, MD, Associate Medical Director, Bakersfield/Kern County; Howard Fullman, MD, Internal Medicine/Gastroenterology, West Los Angeles; Robert Riewerts, MD, Pediatrics, Baldwin Park; Randy Lehmer, MD, Internal Medicine, Orange County; Brian Saunders, MD, Pediatrics/Neonatology, San Diego; Mark Bradburne, MD, Internal Medicine/Pulmonary Medicine, Riverside; Mark Bird, MD, Anesthesiology, Orange County.

the idea to Sid Wolenski, litigation director of the advocate rights group. "He thought it was a wonderful idea," recalled Neri. "He said 'I think you guys have gone from the bottom of the list as a potential target, to the top of the list as being supporters of the movement for the disabled groups.'"

The lawsuit was settled in April 2002. The settlement required Kaiser Permanente to install accessible medical equipment, remove architectural barriers and develop training programs, handbooks and a complaint system to meet the needs of the disabled. Disabled activists called the agreement "historic."

For its part, the Riverside Medical Center soon began executing the plan to improve care for its disabled patients. Explained Neri, "We started by taking steps to identify all the people with disabilities. We then identified their type of disability. Was it mobile, cognitive, hearing or visual? We entered all of this information into the computer so that when the patient called to make an appointment we would be ready for them."

But identifying disabled patients was only part of the solution. The next step was to acquire the equipment to meet their needs. "We came up with a computer model that identified the type and amount of equipment we would need," said Neri. "We even went to manufacturers to redesign some equipment that we especially wanted." The new equipment included a special electronic bed that could lift a patient out of a wheelchair, height-adjustable examination tables, and accessible X-ray and diagnostic equipment.

The methods developed at Riverside and San Francisco to improve health care delivery and access for people with disabilities will serve as a model not just at Kaiser Permanente, but throughout the country.

TAKING CARE OF BUSINESS

The SCPMG Business Administrator is the highest-ranking lay executive in the Medical Group and occupies a unique role in that this position serves in both a staff and line capacity.

The Business Administrator acts as a senior advisor and strategic planner to provide expert and knowledgeable financial and operational advice and consultation to SCPMG leadership and physician staff on issues relating to Kaiser Permanente business and to ensure that SCPMG remains a viable entity. The position is also responsible for the staff in the SCPMG Regional Offices.

Along with the Associate Medical Directors, the SCPMG Business Administrator is a vital part of the Medical Director's Senior Staff. Five talented men have served as Business Administrator during SCPMG's first 50 years:

Jack Croft (1957–1971)
Richard E. Brown (1972–1981)
Peter Szekrenyi (1981–1982)
Richard Barnaby (1982–1989)
Peter Pellerito (1989–present)

A NEW MEDICAL CENTER FOR BALDWIN PARK

By the late 1980s there were more than 170,000 Health Plan members living in the San Gabriel Valley, a heavily populated area east of downtown Los Angeles. For these members, the closest medical centers were in Los Angeles and Bellflower, and San Gabriel Valley residents used both of them. But it was time for the San Gabriel Valley to have its own medical center.

Kaiser Permanente decided to build the new medical center in the San Gabriel Valley city of Baldwin Park and selected a site just east of the San Gabriel Freeway (I-605) and south of the San Bernardino Freeway (I-10). The medical center would be built on a plot of land once occupied by an abandoned drive-in theater.

In July 1989, Dr. Gary Lulejian was asked to lead the efforts to establish the new service area. Dr. Lulejian had joined SCPMG in 1969 as a pediatrician at the Panorama City Medical Center. He went on to serve as Assistant to the Area Associate Medical Director in Panorama City and on the SCPMG Board of Directors.

Satellite medical offices in Montebello, West Covina and Temple City that had been part of the Los Angeles service area now became part of the new Baldwin Park service area. The Temple City office would later be closed. New construction included a medical office in San Dimas and an addition to an existing Mental Health Office in West Covina.

Plans called for the Baldwin Park Medical Center to be built in two phases, with a medical office building to go up first, followed by a hospital building. Construction of a three-story medical office building began in January 1990. The facility opened in August 1991 and housed primary care services, including Family Practice, Obstetrics/Gynecology and Pediatrics. Support services included laboratory, pharmacy, and X-ray departments, as well as administrative offices.

Construction began on the hospital building in June 1991. As the structure rose, it readily became apparent that the Baldwin Park Medical Center was different — the crescent-shaped inpatient tower had a unique "space age" look that set it apart from the other Kaiser Permanente medical centers. Baldwin Park was different inside as well. The new facility featured "Wayfinding," an architectural concept that uses design elements and color to mark pathways and direct the eye to departmental signs and informational directories. "There is a feeling of openness and freshness," said architect Jim Herrington. "This facility is designed to be user-friendly and will certainly offer a more positive experience for all users."[26]

The hospital building was completed in June 1994. But while all the building's medical offices and services would be opened, the hospital floors themselves

TOP LEFT TO RIGHT
Pete Pellerito
Baldwin Park Medical Center groundbreaking
Baldwin Park Medical Center construction site

BOTTOM LEFT TO RIGHT
Aerial view of Baldwin Park Medical Center construction site
Construction crew

remained closed, pending a decision as to whether Kaiser Permanente or another organization would run the hospital. Meanwhile, the hospital floors stood empty for the next four years.

Finally, in February 1998, Gary Lulejian received the go-ahead to open the hospital as a Kaiser Permanente–run facility. Why then? "Because our planned membership growth was greater than our facilities capacity could handle," said Pete Pellerito, SCPMG's Business Administrator.[27] To open the hospital as quickly as possible, Kaiser Permanente entered into a unique labor-management partnership with the key unions that worked with the organization. "The Baldwin Park hospital was the test site to see just how well this labor-management partnership would work," said Dr. Lulejian. "No other Kaiser Permanente facility to date — let alone any other medical facility in the United States — had opened as a team effort between labor and management."[28]

To launch this pioneering effort, executives formed a 20-member labor-management steering committee, including representatives of management, the union, and the physicians. Five unions were included on the committee, representing registered nurses; licensed

Baldwin Park Medical Center

vocational nurses, assistants and housekeeping workers; social workers; laboratory and pharmacy technicians; and nurse anesthetists.

Together, management and labor jointly planned all operations of the new hospital. Working together would require some adjustment on both sides. "Management had to learn to relinquish unilateral control over issues and information that typically fell solely under management purview," recalled Lulejian. "These issues included access to financial information, control over the interview and hiring processes, and selection of equipment and supplies. For their part, union employees had to learn to trust management and work cooperatively to provide the best care for our patients."

The hospital opened on October 7, 1998. Said Lulejian, "I credit the labor-management partnership with enabling us to open the hospital in just seven months. There was considerable commitment and cooperation on both sides to get this hospital open. It usually takes a year and a half to open a hospital — we did it in record time." After the hospital opened, labor and management continued working together to run individual units throughout the facility.

According to Lulejian, both labor and management benefited from the partnership arrangement. "I think the fact that we could sit down and talk to one other was extremely important," said Lulejian. "I think it helped both sides realize that we had many similar problems and challenges and because of that, we were often able to forge a compromise that worked for both of us." According to Pete Pellerito, these initial labor-management partnering efforts at Baldwin Park would have far-reaching implications. "The success of the Baldwin Park experience was one of the cornerstones that the national Labor Management Partnership was built upon. We were excited to use their learnings as a model of expected partnership behaviors for all of Kaiser Permanente."

Dr. Lulejian continued as Area Associate Medical Director in Baldwin Park until his retirement in December 2002.

THE DEATH OF RAY KAY

Ray Kay, SCPMG's first Medical Director and its guiding force for two decades, died in his sleep on January 18, 1997, at 92.

Although it was Sidney Garfield's generosity in giving away his own medical group that enabled SCPMG to become a partnership, it was Ray Kay who guided the partnership through its formative years. Kay took it upon himself to assemble the best physician partners he could find. He helped develop many of the principles of successful group practice that endure today not just at SCPMG, but throughout the country. In 1984, the American Group Practice Association named Drs. Kay and Garfield as co-recipients of an award for outstanding contributions to group practice named in memory of Dr. Russell V. Lee, founder of the Palo Alto Clinic and himself a great promoter of group practice. At a lecture associated with the award ceremony, Kay was introduced by his old friend Irv Klitsner, who called him "one of the pioneers in the truest spirit, who paved the way for prepaid group practice medicine."

In the introduction to Ray Kay's history of SCPMG, Sidney Garfield wrote: "It is said that every great institution is the lengthened shadow of one great man. Since Dr. Kay participated significantly in every step of Kaiser Permanente's development, since he was largely responsible for the concept of our nonprofit entities, and since his unswerving persistence against strong opposition was the major reason for Kaiser Permanente's expansion into Southern California, it can truly be said the Southern California Region exists in his shadow."

CHANGING OF THE GUARD

After serving as Medical Director for ten years, Oliver Goldsmith retired on December 31, 2003. Goldsmith had earned high marks for leading SCPMG through some very difficult times while always keeping the Group focused on its primary goal — high-quality patient care. "I think that over the years that whenever we've had a difficult issue or the Medical Group struggled with a difficult problem [. . .] Oliver was very quick to remind us that the reason we're here is to take care of patients," said Les Zendle.[29] Oliver Goldsmith's "retirement" plans included a return to clinical practice at a community clinic. As he said, "It's my opportunity to pay back."

In November 2002, SCPMG had elected Dr. Jeffrey Weisz as its sixth Regional Medical Director. Dr. Weisz grew up in Detroit and received his medical degree from Wayne State University School of Medicine. He completed his Internal Medicine internship and residency at Henry Ford Hospital in Detroit and a Clinical Hematology/Oncology fellowship at Los Angeles County-USC Medical Center. He then returned to Detroit to enter private practice, but after a year, started "missing the great weather out in Southern California and thought I should return."[30]

In a scenario that echoes Frank Murray's introduction to SCPMG, Weisz also happened to know a Permanente physician, Dr. Norman Hellman, a hematologist practicing at the Panorama City Medical Center. Weisz gave Dr. Hellman a call. As Weisz recalls, "Dr. Hellman said, 'It's a great organization. Why don't you come on out and we'll show you around and maybe we can recruit you.' I flew out, walked up the steps of Panorama City and Norm welcomed me. I met the rest of the Department, then we went from there." Weisz joined the Medical Group in 1978 as a staff hematologist/oncologist in Panorama City. In 1986, he became Physician-in-Charge of the Oncology Section at Woodland Hills.

Weisz's entry into administration wasn't exactly the career path he had intended. "I went to medical school to take care of patients," said Weisz, "but one day, after leaving my busy morning clinic, I happened to speak out at one of our Tuesday conferences regarding how we should best use our education time and that led to me running for the Board of Directors." Weisz represented his Woodland Hills colleagues as an elected Board member for three terms, served as Assistant to the Area Associate Medical Director from 1996 to 1999 and was appointed Area Associate Medical Director of Woodland Hills in 1999. "I never thought in any day and age I would be an administrator, but here I am," said Weisz.

Interestingly, Weisz's comments about not planning to become an administrator are relatively common among SCPMG's physician managers. Said Irwin Goldstein, "When I started, I never thought I would be doing something like this [Associate Medical Director and Physician Manager of Operations] for the bulk of my professional career. Administration wasn't on my mind when I came to the organization. So there are plenty of opportunities for people who want to get into administrative areas."[31] Dr. Weisz himself appreciated the opportunity SCPMG provides to weave administrative duties within a medical career. "Working with the Group offers a great opportunity for young physicians," said Weisz. "They can bond with patients, practice wonderful medicine and if they want to be administrative physicians, they can also blend that with their practice."

In January 2003, as Medical Director-elect, Jeffrey Weisz began working with Oliver Goldsmith, carrying on the tradition of SCPMG's outgoing and incoming Medical Directors working together to ensure a smooth transfer of responsibilities.

As Weisz prepared to take the reins at SCPMG as of January 2004, he described the current status of the medical care business as "tough." He spoke of competition and escalating costs and what he planned to do to meet those challenges. "We're going to have to control our costs," said Weisz, "but I think the biggest thing that's going to separate SCPMG from the outside is improving our service and access. [. . .] That's where I'm going to focus my energy."

When asked for specifics as to how he planned to improve service and access, Weisz cited a program in Woodland Hills that he wanted to expand throughout the Region. He described the program as "taking a proactive stance towards new members. Welcome them into the organization, make it easy for them to bond with a physician and help them move through the system when they first join." Weisz explained that the Woodland Hills Medical Center sent a letter and phoned every new patient over 65 years of age, encouraging them to call and speak with their primary physician — and 98 percent of them did. New patients also received a questionnaire which enabled their physician to quickly involve them in a diabetes clinic, hypertensive clinic, or allergy clinic. New female patients received a

mammogram before they even saw their primary care physician. "This is paying off," said Weisz, who noted that the program had actually been successful in helping Woodland Hills retain Health Plan members who may otherwise have dropped out of the program.

"My vision is that when a new member joins Kaiser Permanente, they'll get efficient, expeditious, compassionate care and then they'll leave and tell 10 or 15 of their friends what a great experience they had. As far as I'm concerned, that's our best advertising. That will help us grow our membership and that will improve our image. That's where we'll need to go."

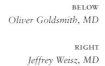

BELOW
Oliver Goldsmith, MD

RIGHT
Jeffrey Weisz, MD

SOUL OF THE HEALER
By Oliver Goldsmith, MD

ON RETURNING TO CLINICAL PRACTICE
I began practicing internal medicine and gastroenterology for the Southern California Permanente Medical Group (SCPMG) in 1969. Over the years, I became interested in medical group management and, in 1989, I left the clinical practice of medicine to take on the role of Area Associate Medical Director for the SCPMG West LA Medical Center. I then had the honor of becoming SCPMG's Regional Medical Director in 1994. Thus, I haven't seen a patient in 13 years.

I'll be retiring as Medical Director at the end of 2003 and am determined to regain some of my medical skills. I have already spent four months at our Inglewood medical offices studying and being proctored. I want to thank Dr. Manny Myers in internal medicine for helping to guide me through this process (ironically, I hired Dr. Myers in 1979 while I was Chief of Medicine at West LA). I'm finding that the medical journals I've skimmed through in the last 13 years haven't prepared me for so many changes — it feels like I've been in outer space. While the interpersonal aspects of medicine have largely stayed the same, the differences in the technical aspects are striking. I would like to describe what I have encountered upon returning to clinical practice.

The nurses, physicians, and staff members are just as wonderful as ever, but now seem very respectful toward me (maybe they've realized I sign their checks — hmm …).

They also seem a lot younger than they were 13 years ago. In contrast, the patients are definitely older these days, and it's very encouraging to see our members living longer, healthier lives. Wow … the number of things that have to be done to meet the needs of elderly patients! Thank goodness the chief of service is scheduling me lightly until I get up to speed.

Additionally, I now have access to an endless array of systems and technology that simply was not in place before 1989. When I was practicing then, a patient might come in and ask for the results of a cholesterol screening performed the previous week. It would take me up to 20 minutes to find those results — getting the patient's name, calling the lab, finding the chart … Now, all of the information available on the computer makes interactions like this effortless. Online test results, online appointment schedules, e-script, e-referral — all of these technologic advances have made managing the care of patients easier. I am also able to make my progress notes appear erudite by taking information from the Permanente Knowledge Connection (PKC).

I've noticed a reduction in the frustration level of our members as a result of access improvement. In the past, patients would spend the first few minutes of their appointment talking about their difficulties with the phones and how long they had to wait to see somebody. This doesn't happen nearly as much as it did in the 70s and 80s. Of course, members can become frustrated, but the remarkable improvement in access, especially on the phones, is a wonderful accomplishment.

The number of drugs, tests, and therapeutic options available to me is simply awesome. I've had to become familiar with new drugs for diabetes and to choose from countless medications — all while trying to follow the clinical guidelines. And for each patient I've seen, there has always been an additional way to provide care — a test, a medication, a referral — whereas 12 to 15 years ago, I would more often have to tell a patient that there was nothing more to be done. There are fewer instances of that now.

In some respects, I feel as if I never stopped practicing medicine. My techniques of physical examination and diagnostic skills have returned to me easily. Also, I haven't lost my bedside manner — my ability to get close to a patient — something of a surprise after more than a decade of dealing exclusively with physicians, staff, and administrators.

More than anything, I realize that I've been missing out on the fun of interacting with patients. Recently, while examining an 84-year-old patient,

I explained to him and his wife that because I was just recently back in practice, another physician would review my work. His wife recognized me because she had been a nurse in the ICU at Kaiser Permanente in the 70s. I appreciated her confidence — as far as she was concerned, I didn't need any help treating her husband. Of course, I can't expect all of my patients to trust me so quickly. But, as always, my demonstration of caring elicits the same level of confidence it did when I was actively practicing medicine. Returning to patient care after being away for so long reminds me how fortunate I am to be a physician.

CELEBRATING FIFTY YEARS

When Ray Kay and Sidney Garfield met at the Los Angeles County Hospital in the early 1930s, they dreamed of practicing with a group of physicians. That dream led to the formation of the Southern California Permanente Medical Group in 1953.

In fifty years, SCPMG has grown from a few dozen physicians to more than 5,600 partners and associates; from caring for just a few thousand people to more than 3.1 million. Certainly that success is a tribute to SCPMG's leadership, to thousands of dedicated physicians and staff, and to a deep commitment to provide the highest possible care to every Kaiser Permanente member.

As SCPMG celebrates its first fifty years, "we are standing tall in Southern California like we never have before," said Oliver Goldsmith. "We are the single most common solution mentioned by anyone to health care in California or this country. We are mentioned in policy, academic, public, and media discussions as a foremost organization in California. We've earned that. Secondly, we have measurably improved the health of our members. We have demonstrated that the group model, whatever its virtues to us as physicians, demonstrably improves people's health. I'm very proud of the people throughout the Medical Group assuming more and more responsibility because the Medical Group is self-governed and that means physicians have to take time out from their practice [. . .] in order to manage and lead the Medical Group. I see a wonderful group of physicians coming along to lead this Medical Group."[32]

SCPMG's first fifty years laid a solid foundation for the next half century…and beyond.

PHOTOGRAPHY CREDITS

Courtesy of the Blackman family
Pages 10, 11
Courtesy of the Ray Kay family
Pages 12, 13, 30, 31
Los Angeles County Hospital, Community Relations
Page 15
Courtesy of Betty Runyen
Pages 18, 19, 32, 32, 155
Stu Levy, photographer
Pages 28–29
The American Medical Association
Page 34
From the collection of Steve Gilford
Pages 36, 40
Steve Spiedel, photographer
Page 102

Jac Flanders, photographer
Page 111
Glen Doll, photographer
Page 132
Matthew Glasser, photographer
Page 152
Fredrik Nilsen, photographer
Pages 158, 159, 160, 161
Alan Weissman, photographer
Page 155 middle
Scott Windus, photographer
Page 164
Jeff Cutting, photographer
Page 171 below
Jonathan Siegel, photographer
Page 171 right

NOTES

CHAPTER 1

1 Asay, Lyal. *Kaiser Permanente in Fontana: Quality Care for One Half Century* (Dr. Asay's personal account, self published, 1993) p. 5.
2 Kay, Ray. "Discovering the Enduring Principles of Group Practice Medicine," *The Permanente Journal,* Winter 2002/Vol.6, No.1.
3 Interview with Sally Garfield Blackman conducted by Steve Gilford.
4 Smillie, John G. *Can Physicians Manage the Quality and Costs of Health Care?: The Story of The Permanente Medical Group* (The Permanente Federation, LLC, 2000, with the express permission of the McGraw-Hill Companies) p. 2.
5 Gilford, interview with Sally Garfield Blackman.
6 Kay, Raymond M. "History of the Kaiser Permanente Medical Care Program," transcript of an oral history interview conducted in 1985 by Ora Huth, Regional Oral History Office, The Bancroft Library, University of California, 1987. p. 3.
7 Kay, interview with Ora Huth, p. 2.
8 Kay, interview with Ora Huth, p. 9.
9 Kay, interview with Ora Huth, p. 13.
10 Kay, interview with Ora Huth, p. 13.
11 Smillie, p. 5.
12 Garfield, Sidney R. Address, Kaiser Foundation Hospitals of Northern California Fifteenth Anniversary, October 19, 1957.
13 Smillie, p. 7.
14 *The Kaiser Story*, Published by Kaiser Industries Corporation, Oakland, California, 1968, p. 7.
15 Garfield, address.
16 Kay, interview with Ora Huth, p. 15.
17 Smillie, p. 17.
18 Garfield, address.
19 Smillie, p. 20.
20 Garfield,, address.
21 Garfield, address.

22 Garfield, address.
23 Garfield, address.
24 Kay, interview with Ora Huth, p. 18.
25 Smillie, p. 31.
26 Smillie, p. 32.
27 Kay, Raymond M. *Historical Review of the Southern California Permanente Medical Group* (Los Angeles, California: Southern California Permanente Medical Group, 1979) p. 3
28 Kay, interview with Ora Huth, p. 21.
29 Kay, interview with Ora Huth, pp. 20–21.
30 Smillie, p. 38.
31 Kay, interview with Ora Huth, p. 22.
32 Kay, interview with Ora Huth, p. 26.
33 Kay, *Historical Review of the Southern California Permanente Medical Group*, p. 3.

CHAPTER 2

1 Gilford, Steve. "#242: On This Date: 1942–43: Kaiser's steel mill in Fontana, CA goes into production" On This Date in KP History, 2002.
2 Smillie, John G., *Can Physicians Manage the Quality and Costs of Health Care?: The Story of The Permanente Medical Group* (The Permanente Federation, LLC, 2000, with the express permission of the McGraw-Hill Companies) p.49.
3 "Fifty Years of Quality Care: The Southern California Region Kaiser Permanente Medical Care Program." November 1992, p. 18
4 Pamphlet: "Health Protection Within the Reach of All" – Kaiser Iron and Steel Company, Fontana, CA, 1943.
5 Kay, Raymond M., "History of the Kaiser Permanente Medical Care Program," an oral history interview conducted in 1985 by Ora Huth, Regional Oral History Office, The Bancroft Library, University of California, 1987. p. 18.
6 Kay, interview with Ora Huth, p. 30.
7 Kay, Ray, "Discovering the Enduring Principles of

Group Practice Medicine," *The Permanente Journal,* Winter 2002/Vol.6, No.1.
8 Kay, interview with Ora Huth, p. 29.
9 Kay, interview with Ora Huth, p. 31.
10 Kay, Raymond M., *Historical Review of the Southern California Permanente Medical Group* (Los Angeles, California: Southern California Permanente Medical Group, 1979) p. 5
11 Kay, *Historical Review of the Southern California Permanente Medical Group*, p. 5.
12 Kay, interview with Ora Huth, p. 31.
13 Smillie, p. 84.
14 Wallin, Ira. All Dr. Wallin comments regarding the San Pedro/Harbor City expansion are from an interview conducted with Dr. Wallin by Steve Gilford, June 9, 1998.
15 Kay, interview with Ora Huth, p. 34.
16 Kay, "Discovering the Enduring Principles of Group Practice Medicine."
17 Marcus, Raymond. Interview with Teri Allen, November 12, 2002.
18 Klitsner, Irv. Interview with Steve Gilford, October 29, 2002.
19 Kay, interview with Ora Huth, p. 37.
20 Marcus, interview with Teri Allen.
21 Kay, interview with Ora Huth, p. 48.
22 Kay, interview with Ora Huth, pp. 73–74.

CHAPTER 3

1 Klitsner, Irv. Videotaped during a presentation with Dr. Ray Kay (Kaiser Permanente MultiMedia Communications #5171), 1987.
2 Sapin, Sam. Interview with Teri Allen, November 18, 2002.
3 "Fifty Years of Quality Care: The Southern California Region Kaiser Permanente Medical Care Program," (No author listed) November 1992, p. 38.
4 Klitsner, videotaped presentation, 1987.

5 Marcus, Raymond. Interview with Teri Allen, November 12, 2002.

6 Foster, Paul. "Outlooks for Medicine 1953." *Bulletin of the Los Angeles County Medical Association,* March 5, 1953. p. 231.

7 Foster, Paul. "Outlooks for Medicine 1953." March 5, 1953. p. 231.

8 Foster, Paul. "Your President Says: Your Complacency is Showing." *Bulletin of the Los Angeles County Medical Association,* June 4, 1953. p. 559

9 "Fifty Years of Quality Care: The Southern California Region Kaiser Permanente Medical Care Program," p. 40.

10 Kay, Raymond M. *Historical Review of the Southern California Permanente Medical Group* (Los Angeles, California: Southern California Permanente Medical Group, 1979) p. 134

11 Kay, Raymond M., "History of the Kaiser Permanente Medical Care Program," an oral history interview conducted in 1985 by Ora Huth, Regional Oral History Office, The Bancroft Library, University of California, 1987. p. 72.

12 Marcus, Raymond. Information regarding Dr. Larry Crowley's visit to Eugene Trefethen provided by Dr. Raymond Marcus in an interview with Steve Gilford, September 26, 2000.

13 Kay, interview with Ora Huth, p. 106.

14 Kay, *Historical Review of the Southern California Permanente Medical Group,* p. 64.

15 Kay, interview with Ora Huth, p. 107.

16 Kay, *Historical Review of the Southern California Permanente Medical Group,* p. 64.

17 Kay, interview with Ora Huth, p. 107.

18 Wallin, Ira. Interview with Steve Gilford, June 9, 1998.

19 Smillie, John G. *Can Physicians Manage the Quality and Costs of Health Care?: The Story of The Permanente Medical Group* (The Permanente Federation, LLC, 2000, with the express permission of the McGraw-Hill Companies) p.100.

20 Smillie, p.102.

21 Kay, *Historical Review of the Southern California Permanente Medical Group,* p. 80.

22 Smillie, p.102.

23 Smillie, p.118.

24 Kay, interview with Ora Huth, p. 83.

25 Gilford, Steve. Information regarding Henry Kaiser's offer to sell the medical care program to the physicians related by Steve Gilford via e-mail to Teri Allen, February 12, 2003.

26 Gilford, Steve. Information regarding the Tahoe Conference and the danger to the medical program's future related by Steve Gilford via e-mail to Teri Allen, February 12, 2003.

27 Kay, interview with Ora Huth, p.84.

28 Smillie, p. 149.

29 Smillie, p. 151.

30 Kay, interview with Ora Huth, p. 69.

31 Kay, interview with Ora Huth, p. 39.

32 Kay, *Historical Review of the Southern California Permanente Medical Group,* p. 7–8.

33 Kay, interview with Ora Huth, p. 56.

34 Fifty Years of Quality Care: The Southern California Region Kaiser Permanente Medical Care Program," p. 31.

35 Wallin, interview with Steve Gilford.

36 Klitsner, Irv. Interview with Steve Gilford, October 29, 2002.

37 Klitsner, interview with Steve Gilford.

38 Kay, *Historical Review of the Southern California*

39 Klitsner, interview with Steve Gilford.

40 Klitsner, interview with Steve Gilford.

41 Kay, interview with Ora Huth, p. 48.

42 Kay, *Historical Review of the Southern California Permanente Medical Group,* pps. 18 and 24.

43 Kay, *Historical Review of the Southern California Permanente Medical Group,* pps. 18 and 42.

44 Kay, *Historical Review of the Southern California Permanente Medical Group,* p. 57.

45 Klitsner, Irving, "Attractions of Permanente to Physicians," For the Third Stanford/Kaiser Permanente Executive Program, September 8, 1982, p. 3.

46 Gilford, Steve. Information about Garfield's "theory of creative shortages" concept related by Steve Gilford (per Gilford's interview with Health Plan executive, Jack Chapman) via e-mail to Teri Allen, February 12, 2003.

47 Kay, interview with Ora Huth, p. 39.

48 Gilford, Steve. Information about the "baby-in-a-drawer" concept related by Steve Gilford via e-mail to Teri Allen, February 12, 2003.

49 Wallin, interview with Steve Gilford.

50 Sapin, Samuel. Oral history interview by John Bluth for the Kaiser Permanente Southern California Region Oral History Project, October 1996, p. 35.

51 *Kaiser Foundation Medical Care Program,* 1962 Report, p.11.

52 Kaiser Foundation Medical Care Program, 1962 Report, p.12.

53 *Kay, Historical Review of the Southern California Permanente Medical Group,* p. 118.

54 Kay, *Historical Review of the Southern California Permanente Medical Group,* p. 115.

55 Kay, interview with Ora Huth, p. 52.

56 Kay, interview with Ora Huth, p. 51.

57 Kay, *Historical Review of the Southern California Permanente Medical Group,* p. 59.

CHAPTER 4

1 Sapin, Samuel. Oral history interview by John Bluth for the Kaiser Permanente Southern California Region Oral History Project, October 1996, p. 69.

2 Klitsner, Irving N. Kaiser Permanente Medical Care Program Southern California Region Oral history interview conducted by Thomas Connors, June 10, 17, 26 and July 1, 1992, p. 145.

3 Kay, Raymond M. "History of the Kaiser Permanente Medical Care Program," an oral history interview conducted in 1985 by Ora Huth, Regional Oral History Office, The Bancroft Library, University of California, 1987. p. 44.

4 *Kay, Raymond M. Historical Review of the Southern California Permanente Medical Group* (Los Angeles, California: Southern California Permanente Medical Group, 1979) p. 112.

5 Sapin, Bluth interview, p. 45.

6 Sapin, Sam. Interview conducted by Teri Allen, January 29, 2003.

7 Sapin, Bluth interview, p. 47.

8 Sapin, Sam. Interview conducted by Teri Allen, November 18, 2002.

9 Klitsner, Irv. Interview with Steve Gilford, October 29, 2002

10 Kay, interview with Ora Huth, p. 124–125.

11 "Fifty Years of Quality Care: The Southern California Region Kaiser Permanente Medical Care Program." November 1992, p. 84.

12 "Fifty Years of Quality Care: The Southern California Region Kaiser Permanente Medical Care Program." November 1992, p. 85.

13 Kay, interview with Ora Huth, p. 45.

14 Kay, *Historical Review of the Southern California Permanente Medical Group,* p. 9–10.

15 "Fifty Years of Quality Care: The Southern California Region Kaiser Permanente Medical Care Program." November 1992, p. 70.

16 Kay, *Historical Review of the Southern California Permanente Medical Group,* p. 10.

17 Kay, Historical *Review of the Southern California Permanente Medical Group,* p. 10.

18 Kay, *Historical Review of the Southern California Permanente Medical Group,* p. 11.

19 Smillie, p. 166.

20 Smillie, p.166.

21 Smillie, p. 166.

22 Gilford, Steve. Information about "The Tehachapi Line" and the agreement between SCPMG and TPMG related by Steve Gilford via e-mail to Teri Allen, February 9, 2003.

23 Kay, *Historical Review of the Southern California Permanente Medical Group,* p. 74.

24 Smillie, p. 168.

25 Gilford, Steve. Information about using Kaiser's Hawaii hospital for hotel guests related by Steve Gilford via e-mail to Teri Allen, February 9, 2003.

26 Smillie, p. 161.

27 Kay, *Historical Review of the Southern California Permanente Medical Group,* p. 74.

28 Smillie, p. 169.

29 Kay, interview with Ora Huth, p. 102.

30 Kay, *Historical Review of the Southern California Permanente Medical Group,* p.11.

31 Kay, *Historical Review of the Southern California Permanente Medical Group,* p. 11.

32 Kay, *Historical Review of the Southern California Permanente Medical Group,* p. 114.

33 Mahrer, Peter. Videotaped comment in "Kaiser Permanente: Yesterday and Today," Kaiser Permanente Audio Visual Services, Production #5225, 1990.

34 Kay, *Historical Review of the Southern California Permanente Medical Group,* p. 21.

35 Kay, *Historical Review of the Southern California Permanente Medical Group,* p. 26.

36 Kay, *Historical Review of the Southern California Permanente Medical Group,* p. 26.

37 Kay, *Historical Review of the Southern California Permanente Medical Group,* p. 26.

38 Kay, *Historical Review of the Southern California Permanente Medical Group,* p. 27.

39 *The Kaiser Story,* Published by Kaiser Industries Corporation. Oakland, California, 1968, p. 7.

40 Gilford, Stephen. "On This Date in KP History," Column #228, 16 Sept., 2002.

41 Crown Point Chalet website, www.crownpointchalet.com. Information provided to website by Steve Gilford

42 Kay, Raymond M. Speech. The American Group Practice Association 35th Annual Meeting. Dallas, Texas. 15 Sept., 1984.

43 Gilford, Steve. Information about the hospital demolition being used in a Magnum PI episode related by Steve Gilford via e-mail to Teri Allen, February 9, 2003.

CHAPTER 5

1 Sapin, Sam. Interview with Teri Allen, January 8, 2003.

2 Asay, Lyal. Kaiser Permanente in Fontana: Quality Care for One Half Century (Dr. Asay's personal account, self published, 1993) p. 33.

3   "Medical Director Retires." Coverage (A pulication of the Kaiser Permanente Southern California Region) October 2, 1981, p. 1.

4   Sapin, Sam. Interview with Jo Ann Lesser, December 10, 2002.

5   Medical Director Retires." Coverage October 2, 1981, p. 1.

6   "Fifty Years of Quality Care: The SouthernCalifornia Region Kaiser Permanente Medical Care Program." November 1992, p. 75.

7   Murray, Frank. "Kaiser Permanente Medical Care Program, Southern California Region Oral History Project" transcript of an oral history interview conducted on December 3 an 4, 1993 by John Bluth, p. 88.

8   Murray, interview with John Bluth, p. 88.

9   Murray, interview with John Bluth, p. 89–91.

10 Murray, interview with John Bluth, p. 92.

11 Murray, interview with John Bluth, p. 95.

12 Sapin, Sam. Information provided via leter to Teri Allen, February 26, 2003.

13 Murray, interview with John Bluth, p. 133.

14 Sapin, Sam. Interview with Teri Allen, January 20, 2003.

15 Sapin, Sam. All information regarding SCPMG's initial medical auditing efforts related by Dr. Sapin via lette to Teri Allen, February 26, 2003.

16 Sapin, Sam. Interview with Teri Allen, March 30, 2003.

17 Sapin, interview with John Bluth, p. 80.

18 Murray, interview with John Bluth, p. 135.

19 Sapin, interview with Teri Allen, March 30, 2003.

20 Sapin, intervie with John Bluth, p. 88.

21 Kaiser Permanente press release, November 18, 1999.

22 Oates, Larry. Information regarding Anaheim provided by Larry Oates, MD in an interview with Teri Allen, April 14, 2003.

23 White, Judy. Interview with Teri Allen, April 9 2003.

24 Asay, Kaiser Permanente in Fontana: Quality Care for One Half Century, p. 33.

CHAPTER 6

1   Seib, Janice. "Frank Murray, MD: A Visionary Leader." *Coverage* (A Publication of Kaiser Permanente Southern California Region) December 1993, p. 4.

2   *"Fifty Years of Quality Care: The Southern California Region Kaiser Permanente Medical Care Program."* November 1992, p. 101.

3   Murray, Frank. "Kaiser Permanente Medical Care Program, Southern California Region Oral History Project" transcript of an oral history interview conducted on December 3 and 4, 1993 by John Bluth, p. 48.

4   Murray, interview with John Bluth, p. 84.

5   Murray, interview with John Bluth, p. 85.

6   Murray, interview with John Bluth, p. 85.

7   Murray, interview with John Bluth, p. 97.

8   Asay, Lyal. *Kaiser Permanente in Fontana: Quality Care for One Half Century* (Dr. Asay's personal account, self published, 1993) p. 33.

9   Sapin, Sam. Interview with Teri Allen, March 30, 2003.

10 Murray, interview with Jo Ann Lesser, December 13, 2002.

11 Murray, interview with John Bluth, p. 108.

12 Murray, interview with John Bluth, pps. 110–111.

13 Murray, interview with John Bluth, p. 111.

14 Murray, interview with Jo Ann Lesser, December 13, 2002.

15 Murray, interview with Jo Ann Lesser, December 13, 2002.

16 Goldstein, Irwin. Interview with Jo Ann Lesser, January 12, 2003.

17 Goldsmith, Oliver. Interview with Jo Ann Lesser, December 5, 2002.

18 Sapin, Samuel. Oral history interview by John Bluth for the Kaiser Permanente Southern California Region Oral History Project, October 1996, pps.103–104.

19 Sapin, interview with John Bluth, p. 108.

20 Sapin, interview with John Bluth, p. 109.

21 Sapin, interview with Jo Ann Lesser, December 10, 2002.

22 Murray, interview with John Bluth, p. 97.

23 Murray, interview with Jo Ann Lesser, December 13, 2002.

24 Murray, interview with John Bluth, pps. 85–86.

25 Murray, interview with John Bluth, p. 86.

26 Murray, interview with John Bluth, p. 170.

27 Murray, interview with John Bluth, p. 171.

28 Murray, interview with John Bluth, pps. 99–100.

29 Murray, interview with John Bluth, p. 100.

30 Murray, interview with John Bluth, pps. 112–113.

31 Seib, Janice. "Frank Murray, MD: A Visionary Leader." *Coverage* December 1993, p. 4

32 Murray, interview with John Bluth, p. 108.

33 Goldstein, Irwin. Interview with Jo Ann Lesser, January 12, 2003.

34 Murray, interview with John Bluth, p. 108.

35 Murray, interview with John Bluth, p. 123.

36 Murray, interview with John Bluth, p. 124.

37 Sapin, interview with John Bluth, p. 113.

38 Sapin, interview with John Bluth, p. 114.

39 Sapin, interview with John Bluth, p. 116.

40 Sapin, interview with John Bluth, p. 116.

41 Murray, interview with John Bluth, p. 126.

42 Sapin, interview with John Bluth, p. 114.

43 Murray, interview with John Bluth, p. 126.

44 Ruderman, Joseph. All comments from Dr. Ruderman about Woodland Hills made during an interview with Teri Allen, April 15, 2003.

45 Ruderman, Joseph. All comments from Dr. Ruderman about Bakersfield made during an interview with Teri Allen, April 15, 2003.

46 Ryder, Ann. All comments from Ann Ryder made during an interview with Teri Allen, April 29, 2003.

47 Neri, Michael A. All comments from Dr. Neri made during an interview with Teri Allen, April 10, 2003.

48 Murray, interview with John Bluth, p. 139.

49 Murray, interview with John Bluth, p. 138.

50 Murray, interview with John Bluth, p. 140.

51 Smillie, John G. *Can Physicians Manage the Quality and Costs of Health Care?: The Story of The Permanente Medical Group* (The Permanente Federation, LLC, 2000, with the express permission of the McGraw-Hill Companies) p. 49.

52 Smillie, p. 54.

53 Smillie, p. 55.

54 Gilford, Steve. Information regarding Sidney Garfield's transfer of the Medical Groups to the partners and the value of those groups, related by Steve Gilford via e-mail to Teri Allen, February 5, 2003.

55 Kay, Raymond M. *Historical Review of the Southern California Permanente Medical Group* (Los Angeles, California: Southern California Permanente Medical Group, 1979) p. 17.

56 Smillie, p. 68.

57 Smillie, p. 223.

58 Sidney R. Garfield, MD 1906-1984" *Coverage* (A Publication of Kaiser Permanente Southern California Region) February, 1985.

CHAPTER 7

1   Goldsmith, Oliver. Speech to SCPMG Board of Directors, 1994

2   Frankl, Harold. Interview conducted by Jo Ann Lesser, December 13, 2002.

3   Goldsmith, Oliver. Interview conducted by Teri Allen, April 17, 2003. All quotes from Dr. Goldsmith are from the Allen interview unless otherwise indicated.

4   Frankl, interview with Jo Ann Lesser.

5   Murray, Frank. Interview conducted by Jo Ann Lesser, December 13, 2002.

6   Goldsmith, Oliver. Speech to SCPMG Board of Directors, 1994

7   Goldsmith, speech reprinted in *Partners News*, March 1994.

8   Goldsmith, speech reprinted in *Partners News*, March 1994.

9   Goldsmith, Oliver. Speech to SCPMG Board of Directors, 1996.

10 Goldsmith, Oliver. Speech to SCPMG Board of Directors, 2001.

11 Goldsmith, Oliver. Speech to SCPMG Board of Directors, 1997.

12 Zendle, Les. Interview conducted by Teri Allen, April 17, 2003.

13 Goldsmith, Oliver. Speech to SCPMG Board of Directors, 1999.

14 Goldsmith, Oliver. Speech to SCPMG Board of Directors, 1999.

15 Goldsmith, Oliver. Speech to SCPMG Board of Directors, 2003.

16 Goldsmith, Oliver. Speech to SCPMG Board of Directors, 2002.

17 Zendle, Les. All comments by Dr. Zendle related to Quality and Service were relayed to Teri Allen via e-mail, June 30, 2003.

18 Cotterell, Adrienne. All comments by Adrienne Cotterell related to Quality and Service made during an interview conducted by Teri Allen, June 5, 2003.

19 Goldsmith, Oliver. Speech to SCPMG Board of Directors, 1996.

20 Goldsmith, Oliver. Speech to SCPMG Board of Directors, 1997.

21 Sapin, Samuel. Interview conducted by Teri Allen, July 19, 2003.

22 Petitti, Diana. All comments from Dr. Petitti made during an interview with Teri Allen, July 18, 2003.

23 Marcus, Ray. Interview conducted by Jo Ann Lesser, December 10, 2002.

24 Goldsmith, Oliver. "Culturally Competent Care," *The Permanente Journal,* Winter 2000/Vol. 4, No.1.

25 Neri, Michael. All comments from Dr. Neri made during an intervie with Teri Allen, April 10, 2003.

26 "A Model for the Future: New Medical Center Redefines State of the Art" Coverage (A Publication of Kaiser Permanente Southern California Region) Spring, 1990, p. 2.

27 Pellerito, Peter. All comments from Mr. Pellerito relayed to Teri Allen via e-mail, July 22, 2003.

28 Lulejian, Gary. All comments from Dr. Lulejian made during an interview with Teri Allen, May 29, 2003.

29 Zendle, Les. Interview conducted by Jo Ann Lesser, December 9, 2002

30 Weisz, Jeffrey. Interview conducted by Jo Ann Lesser, December 5, 2002. All Dr. Weisz quotes from the Lesser interview.

31 Goldstein, Irwin. Interview conducted by Jo Ann Lesser, January 12, 2003.

32 Goldsmith, Oliver. Interview conducted by Jo Ann Lesser, December 9, 2002.